PRIVATE AND CONTROVERSIAL

Private and Controversial

LORD PLATT M.D.

Cassell · London

CASSELL & COMPANY LTD
35 Red Lion Square, London WC1R 4SJ
Sydney, Auckland
Toronto, Johannesburg

First published 1972

I.S.B.N. 0 304 29010 6

Printed in Great Britain by
Northumberland Press Ltd,
Gateshead
F.472

To my fellow Opsimaths

Contents

Preface

What can I say in a preface? Certainly nothing about the book, for if it is worth saying it is already written there, and to judge it for himself, or herself, will be part of the interest, and at times the fun, which I hope the reader will derive from it.

Only my gratitude remains to be expressed, to all that has helped to make my life seem somehow worthwhile (to me at any rate). To my family, my friends and my patients. And to music. I must also acknowledge my sincere thanks to Esther Eisenthal of Cassell who has worked hard with me on the manuscript. All the material is new, but of course I have spoken and written on some of the topics which are here discussed and in some cases I have borrowed freely from published articles. For permission to do this I have pleasure in thanking the Controller of Her Majesty's Stationery Office for extracts from Hansard; the editor of *The British Medical Journal* for some parts of articles in their 'Personal View' columns and extracts from my Harveian Oration to the Royal College of Physicians; the editor of *The Lancet* for similar permission; the editor of *Health* who first published some of the material written for chapters 5 and 6 of this book.

A letter from a friend some years ago ended with the words 'I see that like me you are an opsimath'. I reached for my *Concise Oxford* and therein read 'one who learns late in life'.

1. The Family

In his famous autobiography, Benvenuto Cellini remarks that he was born in 1500 and therefore never had to calculate his age. I have avoided a good deal of mental arithmetic by being born in 1900, and the reader also may find it convenient. No great mathematical skill is required, for instance, to realize that I was eighteen in 1918 and forty-five in 1945.

Apart from my brother's career as an engineer and mine as a doctor, neither medicine nor science appears on either side of the family or in our children. My brother rightly points out here that engineers (like doctors) are only part-scientists, but also (like doctors) are partly artists and craftsmen. Some of my grandchildren have leanings towards science and my second cousin Portia is also a doctor, as I discovered by accident in 1945.

The three traits which come out with rather astonishing frequency in the family are Music, the Stage, and the Wanderlust. My great-grandfather Samuel Holman (1786-1852) was a member of the Devonshire Holman family, in his case the Silverton branch. I have his family tree, which is not particularly notable, back to the late sixteenth century. Many of his ancestors seem to have been local worthies and are described as church-wardens. Samuel ran away to sea and later returned to London penniless.

It is said by my aunt Agnes, from whom I obtained most of the lore pertaining to this branch of the family, that he danced the hornpipe in the London streets (to what accompaniment is unknown to me) and his histrionic talent was recognized by a passer-by. This was none other than the great and fabulous Edmund Kean who found great-grandfather a place on the stage at Covent Garden—in those days mostly used for plays, including

I

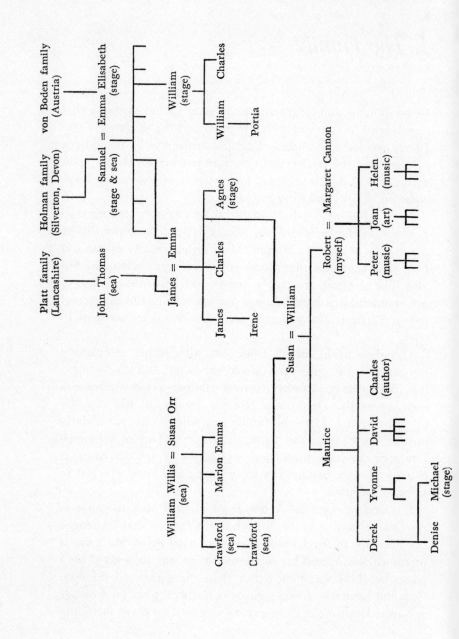

Shakespearian plays, rather than for opera. It seems likely that Kean, who himself had roamed the world as a cabin boy and had known what it was to be penurious, was attracted to Samuel Holman as a man with whom he had much in common. How long Samuel remained on the stage I do not know, but the important thing is that there he met Emma Elisabeth von Boden whom he married at St Martin-in-the-Fields in 1827.

She boasted of having played important Shakespearian parts but I can find no record at the Victoria and Albert Museum of her taking more than minor roles. She was also a singer. According to Agnes her grandfather was a refugee from the Austrian court and a minor member of the Habsburg Royal Family. He settled in England where his son became articled to a firm of solicitors and eloped with an heiress who was one of their clients. Unfortunately her parents did not approve of the younger von Boden and his heiress was cut off with the proverbial shilling. In my Walter Mitty moods I count myself related to all the royal families of nineteenth-century Europe and pretender to the throne of Austria; doubtless also related to the Kings of Prussia, the Margraves of Brandenburg, the Rasoumovsky's and all the other great patrons of Bach, Mozart and Beethoven. Great-grandmother also claimed to have been courted at the stage door by George IV himself, perhaps during his regency period.

The census of 1841 shows the family living in Long Acre, Samuel being now a coach-builder. He later moved to Paulton's Square, Chelsea, to a house which still stands in this almost unspoilt square. He left a comfortable fortune but shared it out to his numerous children. Amongst these was my grandmother Emma who married James Platt. A kindly woman though I think a sad one, she held the affection of her grandchildren in a somewhat distant way for, although we all lived in Hampstead, we did not see very much of her.

Before we come to James Platt we should take notice of some other Holmans, starting with Samuel's son William, my great uncle. He inherited the histrionic talent of the von Bodens and, although described as a cabinet-maker, he spent most of his time and all of his money producing and acting plays before he migrated to Australia. It is said by Agnes that my grandfather James Platt paid William Holman's passage to Australia because he was tired of paying his debts. In Australia he carried on his trade and certainly his Shakespearian acting. He had two sons, one of whom became the Hon. William Holman (junior), Barrister at Law and first Socialist Premier of New South Wales.

The other brother, Charles, migrated to South America and was lost to the family for twenty years. He turned up in England during the 1914-18 war somewhat the worse for wine, women and song (though in truth I know nothing of his talent as a singer). He had made fortunes and gambled them away and was reputed to be an expert with a revolver. It is said that once, as a result of some escapade, he wandered with a companion through the backwoods of one of the South American countries to evade the law; his companion shot himself and Charles went on alone. He was a wonderful companion to a teenage youngster like myself during the few months in which (to my father's great embarrassment) he lived near us; father had found some rooms in a cottage for him in Grindleford, where we then lived. He taught me, amongst other things, how the experts cheat at cards. His brother the Hon. William, at father's urgent request, paid for Charles's removal to Australia, where his presence must have been kept a close secret for he was no proper person to be the brother of a Prime Minister.

Only thirty years later did I discover that Will Holman's only daughter Portia (note the Shakespearian tradition maintaining itself) had no knowledge that she had ever had an uncle, yet she must have been well into her teens when Charlie returned to Australia. Portia came to England, read a degree in Economics at Newnham and later qualified in Medicine with a view to becoming a psychiatrist. Her career was interrupted for a time by her involvement in the Spanish Civil War. She took up child psychiatry successfully and was on the staff of the Elizabeth Garrett Anderson Hospital. As far as I knew in 1945 she was still in Australia and I had no idea that she had even qualified in Medicine, for both her father and mine had died and I had lost touch with the family. One day, towards the end of the Second World War, at Southern Army Head-quarters, Bangalore, I was looking up someone in the Medical Directory, and suddenly the name Portia Holman attracted my eye. Correctly thinking it unlikely that there could be two persons of that name I wrote to her at once to ascertain that she was in fact my second cousin. It was some time later in conversation that I discovered the existence of her uncle Charlie was unknown to her.

James Platt, senior, my grandfather, like all people I know of the name, belonged to the Platt family whose origins seem to spring from the region of Oldham on the Lancashire–York-shire border. I have never traced my relationship to other mem-bers of the family, such as Sir Harry or Sir William Platt, because great-grandfather Platt, like Holman, left the family home for a seaman's life and returned penniless to London. I know nothing of him except that his name was John Thomas and that he found employment as a Spitalfields weaver.

Early origins in the Lancashire textile industry may have influenced him in this, and, more distantly, influenced his son James (my grandfather Platt). James borrowed a modest sum and set up a prosperous wholesale woollen business: at the beginning of the century the name of James Platt and Company of 77 St Martin's Lane was known to the whole woollen trade and James had a comfortable mansion, Rookwood, in Hamp-stead (now pulled down and replaced by flats). He was at one time thought to be worth half a million pounds, but, alas, in his late seventies he fell a victim to the evil influence and machinations of Horatio Bottomley, lost all his money in speculation and was made a bankrupt. Luckily his wife's small legacy from the Holmans kept them in modest circumstances in their old age.

I remember all four of my grandparents well, as they were all conveniently born between 1832 and 1834 in the short reign of William IV, and all survived to their late seventies or early eighties by which time I was adolescent. I always think of them as having been contemporary with Brahms although of course he lived to be only sixty-seven. James Platt was, to us boys, an austere man who said or did nothing to attract a child. You just didn't know what to say to him and he gave you no help. Granny seemed to dry up in his presence. His occasional birthday letters to me were formal to a degree, very short, offering some brief homily and then ending with a message to convey to my father, which seemed to be the real purpose of the letter. But Agnes at least loved him even if his wife and sons did not warm to him. If it is true, as I have heard, that he kept a mistress for many years, he must have had warmth somewhere even if it was directed into the wrong channels.

Bankruptcy must have been a terrible blow to him for in his prime he had written books on business methods and clearly considered himself to be a stalwart and prudent person. The Holman aunts, sisters of my grandmother Platt, were reputed to be prudes. In their Victorian respectability they were ashamed of their mother, the exciting Emma Elisabeth von Boden, who, in her old age, with regrettable indiscretion would enliven and disgrace the family circle by bursting into song and reciting her stage parts of years ago.

The four children of James Platt and Emma Holman were all notable in their way but need be but briefly mentioned. The three sons, James, Charles and William (my father) were all put into the business but given a salary and no authority. James senior held the reins. None of them was really interested in the business, perhaps for that reason. James (junior) became a scholar and a linguist, and spent much of his time in the Reading Room of the British Museum. I have heard him discourse in Persian in his own house; all European languages were known to him, as well as many Eastern ones, and he was an authority on North American Indian and Eskimo dialects. He used to say that it was only the first twelve languages which presented any difficulty. Murray consulted him freely on difficult problems of etymology and he is mentioned in several of the prefaces to volumes of the O.E.D.

It is said that after his death, Murray asked his widow if he could look at James's library. No doubt he was expecting to see

an immense collection of scholarly works in all languages. He
was disappointed. Any part of Uncle James's immense knowledge which was not stored in his own brain was in the British
Museum.

James travelled widely usually pretending to be a Norwegian;
he said it was cheaper since the British were exploited. He had
a huge beard and wore a cloak and was once arrested in Madrid
as an anarchist. He also visited, with some well-known London-
ers of the time, little frequented parts of London's East End
and Dockland, including Chinese opium dens. James's only
child, Irene, did not follow him as a scholar but developed great
athletic prowess rare in our family. She was a champion at
tennis and only recently she holed-in-one in a local golf cham-
pionship at the age of seventy-one.

Charles, equally disinterested in the family business, became
expert in chess and had a collection of carved ivory chessmen
which was famous in its day. He wrote a book about cats,
another of his interests.

My father, William Platt, was the only one, in my view, who
worked loyally for the business until it collapsed, but he too
found his main interests elsewhere, notably in music (he published a number of minor compositions), history, literature and
geology. He published *A Popular Geology* and wrote a number
of novels and poems. When the business did collapse he and my
mother moved into Grindleford, Derbyshire, where they started
a co-educational boarding-school.

Father was somewhat eccentric, but devoted to children, and
quite unable to curb his zest for teaching. He had an enormous
general knowledge, perhaps because, like many other really well-
informed people I have known, he had never received a formal
university education. Had he done so he would doubtless have
won high honours in some narrow and possibly useless field of
scholarship. He remained young and vigorous to the end of his
days. In some ways he never really grew up. I remember quite
recently saying to a friend that he could dive and swim at
seventy-six, and only gave it up then because he died.

Agnes, the youngest and only girl of my father's generation,

was stage-struck from childhood but her Victorian parents refused to let her follow the profession of her von Boden grandmother. She became a reader of plays and an adviser on stage
production and related matters. Her book, entitled *Anonymous*,
tells of the stage characters whom she had known in the late
nineteenth century. A voluminous correspondent, she took to
typing all her letters as her handwriting was so appalling. She
is the only person I have known who could practically type
illegibly, for she never corrected mistakes, her ribbons were
worn, her type uncleaned, and, if temporarily short of paper,
she would put the typed page back into the machine and type
crosswise above what was already written.

Agnes tried marriage for a short time but it was not a success.
Eccentric to a greater degree than any other member of the
family she also inherited the weakness of dying in penury; she
had given away most of the money she had ever earned to
talented young stage friends whom she felt were in need. In
later years she lived in a caravan in a field in Devonshire with
two West Highland terriers. A kind woman in a neighbouring
farm looked after her when she was too ill or frail to fend for
herself or to buy food. I think my brother and I contributed a
pound or two per week for some years, but we never gave her
much at a time for she would have passed it on to some poor
soul whom she deemed more needy than herself.

My mother was a remarkable woman but her side of the
family being less eccentric than the Holman–von Boden stock
will come in for less description. She was born in County
Armagh where her mother was staying with relatives at the
time, my grandfather being, as usual, away. The family were
North of Ireland Scots from Loughgall (Armagh) but mother
was brought up almost entirely in Scotland. Her father (my
grandfather Willis) had some job which took him around the
world and was away for long periods, but I don't think he was
a seaman by profession; he was probably some kind of courier.
A charming, genial man, beloved by his grandchildren and
chiefly remembered for his large grey beard and his ability
to play the flute, he would make sly remarks about granny

Willis with a wink of the eye when she was not looking. She was an austere church-going woman of whose many virtues, Gibbon might have said, tolerance was not the most conspicuous. But as I grew older I soon realized that it was the stalwart, inflexible character of granny rather than the attractive, easy-going nature of grandfather which accounted for my mother's academic success and the excellent Scottish education which all the family received. When grandfather retired from whatever he had been doing at sea, he became the incumbent (if that is the term) of the County Hotel in Forfar, which, being then a temperance hotel—for Granny would have countenanced none other—was not a financial success. They retired to Tayport, supported in their old age by small contributions from such members of the family as could afford them.

Their eldest child Crawford went to sea and became a Captain in the British India line. He was a fine and brave man. He, too, saw little of his wife since he would be away for three years at a time. My brother and I enjoyed his seaman's tales on his occasional visits to London and the half-sovereign which always mysteriously found its way into our portions of the Christmas pudding. He had no particular taste for scholarship and, when they were children, my mother would do his Latin exercises for him while he was down at the docks watching the ships go in and out. His son, in turn, went to sea.

My mother's two sisters both married impoverished Scottish artists, quite well known in their day. Emma, the youngest, and her husband Alec Grieve, who was a close friend of Keir Hardie, lived in a small cottage beside the lighthouse (West Lights) at Tayport (Fife). The memory of the smell of oil-paint, oil-lamps, and Alec's cut twist tobacco is still evocative as only memories of smells can be.

Emma gave lessons on the violin. She was everyone's favourite and had many sweethearts in her young days, some of whom I met at her funeral. All three sisters and their mother lived into their seventies though all developed cancer of the breast. Alec died in his fifties leaving Emma a widow. I always thought their marriage, though childless (or because childless?) was one of the few really happy ones I have known although their joint income must often have been barely a hundred pounds a year. Emma's attractions were by no means extinguished with age for, long after Alec died, she acquired a male friend much younger than herself, who would stay so late into the night as to give rise to gossip among the neighbours.

My mother took a degree at St Andrews University, or rather an L.L.A. (Licentiateship in Arts) since women were not allowed to take degrees in those days. She went to Lewes in Sussex to teach at a private school. Her headmistress lent her the money (which she quickly repaid) to become properly trained as a teacher at the Cambridge Training College (now Hughes Hall) under its first principal, Miss E. P. Hughes. She was one of their star students and stayed on as a lecturer, won a scholarship to Paris, became the first woman to be an Inspector of Schools and was well known in education circles. Later in life she founded, with my father, the school in Grindleford. Mother could play the piano competently and had a fine contralto voice.

Of present members of the family I shall say little except to illustrate the maintenance of the Music–Stage–Wanderlust complex of the family. My brother's grandson was 'the boy' in Brecht's *Galileo* at the Mermaid Theatre at the age of twelve. He and his parents did not know there had been actors in the family until I told them. My own son is Professor of Music in Dunedin, New Zealand, and produces music and opera. His children carry on the musical tradition, his son having earned on occasion up to twenty pounds a week in a pop group as bass guitar while still at school. His girls have both appeared on the stage. My elder daughter's artistic talent is in pictorial art (Slade School) rather than music but my younger daughter took a degree in Music and went to Australia where she has also appeared on the stage. Their mother had a fine soprano voice and used to sing in concerts and in madrigals, and their own children all show musical talent.

My own musical interest has been life-long. Though I cannot perhaps claim a full share of the wanderlust, my journeys round the world being occasioned by the war or by professional invitations, I can, I think, claim that I have never kept at the same job for more than ten years at a time in the forty-nine since I qualified. My longest spell, 1946-65, as Professor of Medicine in Manchester, was interrupted (1957-62) by becoming President of the Royal College of Physicians of London.

2. Student Days

Sir Geoffrey Jefferson once told me about a conversation he had at the house of Wilder Penfield in Canada, when these two and a few other famous medical men were sitting together, and someone said 'If you were asked to recall some apparently trivial event which may have greatly influenced your life, what would you say?' Geoffrey posed this question to me and a memory, probably dating from 1917, flashed up at once from the unconscious mind.

The computer qualities of the human memory system with its millions of cross-references are indeed remarkable, for I had hardly thought of this event in the forty or more years since it occurred. My answer was 'The original buildings of Sheffield University form a quadrangle in the centre of which is a pond and a fountain. There is therefore no path directly across the quadrangle and to reach the other side you must go either to the right or to the left. If your destination is the centre of the buildings opposite it makes no difference which path you choose. I was a somewhat precocious student having started the medical course at the age of sixteen, and was younger than most of my fellow students. I remember entering the quad with five or six others one day and they were beginning to veer to the right side. Suddenly I thought "If I go to the left they'll follow me." I did, and they did.'

This would be before I started the clinical part of the medical course. It must be confessed that the pre-clinical part of the course (that is, Anatomy and Physiology) did not then interest me very much. Most of the physiology I know I learnt after qualification. There were many distractions. The ghastly war dragged on and most of the young men I knew were going into the services. Many of them never returned. I felt a very strong compulsion to do the same. Under these circumstances I found it difficult to take my future seriously. In fact I had enlisted in 1916, giving a false age, but on my being called up my parents revealed the true facts and I was released with a charge of 'False attestation and misappropriation of the King's Monies' (having accepted the customary shilling on enlistment).

In 1918 I interrupted my medical studies and went to an officer cadet battalion at Oxford, where I succeeded in becoming a Second Lieutenant in the Infantry. I very soon discovered that by volunteering to sing in the choir, and therefore attend choir practice, I was able to avoid the unwelcome inspection and discipline of a military church parade. The anecdote which springs to my mind of my military days in Oxford is of our Sergeant-Major who one Monday morning gave us a homily on the regrettable state of the river on Sunday afternoons, which he feared would bring the army into bad repute. 'Nothing but Officers' bottoms and ripples on the water' was what he actually said. I recall that sexual experiment was not an invention of the universities of the 1960s.

The life of a junior officer in the Infantry in those days was not very long and it may have been the influenza epidemic of 1918 (which killed some of my comrades) which saved my life, since I was still convalescent when the Armistice was signed and my posting to France had been postponed.

I realize now that my course as a medical student was a series of calculated risks. Although born and brought up in London, my parents having moved to Derbyshire when I was a boy, I trained in Medicine at Sheffield University where the medical faculty, further depleted by the war, was a very small one. I knew all my fellow students and was quite certain that with a minimum of application to work I could pass at least as well as they, and these somewhat priggish and immodest calculations paid off.

I passed in Anatomy and Physiology in the spring after the war had ended and went on to do clinical work at the hospital. I stood in a small group round the bed of a real patient for the first time. I even remember that he had pyloric stenosis. I seemed to know at once that the drudgery of the pre-clinical subjects was over and that I was destined to be a physician, and delighted at the prospect. But having decided to be a physician my interest in Obstetrics and Gynaecology, which I did not intend to practise, was correspondingly diminished and the technique of the calculated risk was again put into action.

For three months we had to attend the Women's Hospital and be personally present at twenty confinements. It seemed to me that the subject, at any rate at the standard required for the M.B., was an extremely limited one which anyone with moderate intelligence could pass if he was content to do a few weeks' swotting towards the end of his course. I therefore spent the minimum of time attending the clinics and lectures though I turned up regularly, by night or day, to witness the birth of twenty-one babies (the series included a twin pregnancy).

The remainder of the time I spent practising the piano and I suppose I averaged four hours a day during those three months. In Medicine, however, and in Pathology, which I deemed to be a subject valuable to physicians, I was very much more assiduous and won two gold medals. These I promptly weighed in water and in air to see whether their specific gravity matched up to that of good quality gold. They passed the test.

I should perhaps refer briefly to two of the other important influences in my life, at that time just after the war. First, that I was deeply in love with Lucie and we used to dance nearly every evening and, second, that I was continuing to have lessons on the 'cello as well as on the piano. These further distractions necessitated the full application of my policy of getting through examinations on the minimum amount of work in any subject which, unlike Medicine, did not inspire me to higher efforts.

I must also say a word or two about one of the students with whom I shared lodgings for a time and who certainly influenced me. He was a year or two my senior and had, I think, been excused military service on account of his sight. It may seem extraordinary, but he was the first person who really taught me to read books seriously for the sake of learning from them and improving my mind. I have often noted how well-read are people with myopia; I suppose they find the world around them less distracting. Amongst the books to which he introduced me were Freud's *Introductory Lectures on Psychoanalysis*, and his *Psychopathology of Everyday Life*. Probably few medical students of that day read Freud at all. Our instruction in mental illness consisted only of a few attendances at the local asylum where we saw people who were definitely and unequivocally mad. The niceties of diagnosis were considered at some length but no one told us anything about treatment. My friend was one of those pleasant though rare people who are very clever but seem to have no ambition. He could have taken higher qualifications with great ease but never did so.

Later in my medical course I changed my lodgings several times. One of my landladies was a handsome and passionate woman but her husband, Sid, seemed singularly inappropriate; he was a somewhat coarse man, while she was sensitive and rather refined. (This probably only meant that she liked to hear my piano-playing, though I know my playing would not have compared in standard with that of many young people of today. This was before electric recordings and radio had brought the playing of great musicians into every home.)

Also in the same digs, some distance from the city, was another medical student who was older than most of us because he had already attempted an Arts degree. He was a brilliant fellow and a great raconteur, but had little taste for serious study. He gave me my first introduction to compulsive alcoholism; he would be teetotal for weeks at a time and then start drinking more and more, coming back to the digs showing little sign of having drunk to excess, but somehow I always knew. I used to warn him, but it was no use. Within the next day or two he would disappear altogether and when he had been missing for some days his father, an important person in local government, would seek me out and ask me to find him with the message that if he would come home all would be forgiven and his debts would be paid. My memory, which may be imperfect, tells me that this happened regularly, that I always seemed to know where to find him and that his debts were always considerable.

Eventually he qualified in Medicine and married a strong-minded woman who kept him successfully away from his alcoholic habits until he died many years later.

In the same lodgings was a figure whom we called 'the Hero'. We rarely saw him for we did not share the same rooms. He was back from the war with a decoration and had been seriously wounded in the stomach. He ascribed his recovery to astuteness on his part. After he had been wounded the doctors had told him he could have anything he liked to eat or drink. However, he had noted that other people who had been similarly wounded were on a strict milk regime and he realized, possibly correctly, that the unexpected liberality of the doctors in his own case was due to the fact that they thought he had no hope of recovery. So, he told me, 'For the only time in my life I said I would have milk.'

One day when I was in my room alone, cutting some of my lectures and playing the piano, the lady of the house came to consult me. The gist of the conversation, and she made her meaning quite clear, was that she wanted to murder Sid, whom she thought was an unfeeling scoundrel with no understanding of love and romance. She discussed with me various poisons with which she might achieve her objective. I suppose this was my first real consultation. I remember feeling that a little quick thinking was required and that I might find myself in a difficult position if it became known that I had given her appropriate and efficient advice. I dealt with the situation by telling her how easily the cause of death could be discovered. That she was absolutely in earnest I never had any reason to question.

Periodically there would be rows between Sid and his wife or between Sid and the Hero; voices would be raised and furniture literally hurled about. On Saturday nights we used to keep as many cups, saucers, glasses and plates as possible in our sitting-room without letting them go back to the kitchen for washing, otherwise there would be a considerable shortage of crockery on Sunday morning.

One night, after there had been loud noises, shouting and scuffling, the Hero came running up to my room and asked me to come downstairs where Sid was lying on the floor, apparently unconscious. 'There,' he said, 'I've done that, have a look at him.' He thought Sid was dead, but fortunately (at any rate for Sid) he was only temporarily knocked out and was beginning to come round by the time my expert advice was sought. That, I suppose, was my second consultation. Although much tempted to stay on in these lodgings to see what happened, discretion overruled my taste for excitement on that occasion, as examinations were imminent; I found lodgings elsewhere and never heard the sequel.

My new lodgings were rather more expensive but probably a good deal safer. They were guarded over by a stout genial woman called Martie, whose enormous bosom would literally bounce when we told her funny stories, which we did quite often. There must have been seven or eight lodgers including myself, a law student and a married couple who occupied a suite of their own. He had been badly wounded but was making a good recovery. His wife was young and beautiful. She told me that when he came home on leave their love-making was so intense that she couldn't wear a low-necked dress for many weeks— she would be covered with tooth marks where he had bitten her in their ecstasy. This impressed me very much at the time and I was very envious of the young man who could make love so passionately with this beautiful woman.

Thinking of these formative years I realize how early in my life women began to confide in me and to talk to me without embarrassment on intimate matters. Of course I have always found it equally easy to talk to women. I think this has been a great asset to me as a physician, but it is an asset which can be dangerous and the temptation to let friendship and intimacy develop is sometimes overwhelming and occasionally irresistible. Although this has never happened between me and a woman patient, I have never been able to develop an attitude of aloofness or detachment which would enable me to keep outside the emotional situations of my patients, be they men, women or children. I have had some rare but memorable conversations with dying people, for instance, and do not believe they could have occurred between a patient and a doctor who was not in some way emotionally involved. I therefore do not subscribe to the view that medical students should be trained to cultivate emotional detachment as if it were a virtue.

Turning now from personal reminiscence to a more serious note on medical education—what major change has taken place in fifty years? The short answer is 'none'. Detail and content are of course different, in some cases very different. Much will be said in subsequent chapters about modern techniques of investigation and their consequences, about research and experiment, and the conquest of bacterial and some other diseases. Facts change, and as they do so we discard the old and teach the new. Pulmonary tuberculosis is now relatively rare and, in the early stages, an easily curable disease; but to be taught this, instead of being taught, as I was, that it is a common disease, which, especially in young adults, often progresses relentlessly to a fatal termination, does not require any fundamental change in medical education. Koch's discovery of the tubercle bacillus dates from 1882, and the infectivity, prevalence and pathology of pulmonary tuberculosis were all well known to us.

We knew that myxoedema was thyroid deficiency and we cured it with thyroid extract (first used by Murray, *c.* 1891) without knowing what the active principle of thyroid extract was or how it worked. Now we use thyroxin or tri-iodothyronine for the same purpose, and still do not know how they work, and the chemical composition of thyroxin, discovered by Harington in the 1930s, is unknown by the great majority of doctors who nevertheless use it properly, rationally and responsibly in their daily practice.

Operations on the heart and lungs were practically unknown in the 1920s, anaesthetics were primitive, X-ray examinations elementary and unreliable, but new medical techniques simply replace older methods and alter the content, rather than the nature, of medical education. The improved understanding of the nature of disease has added to what must be learned, but has at the same time simplified some of the concepts of disease. The problems posed by increasing specialization become ever more acute, but are not new. There were already heart specialists, lung specialists and neurologists long before 1920, and most of London's special hospitals for the eyes, for the skin, for cancer, for women and for children were built in the nineteenth century.

For two and a half years, from 1965 to 1968, I was a member of the Royal Commission on Medical Education. We discussed the entry into medical schools, how much science and how much practice should be taught and how knowledge and competence should be assessed, how medical schools should be organized and how many doctors were needed. But no one questioned—indeed how could they?—that medicine must be learned by instruction, by practical work, by example, and by demonstration, and that a basis of scientific knowledge and thinking was required.

Now, as in 1920, professors argue about what is an adequate scientific basis, and how it should be taught. Even the basis has, of course, altered factually. No one taught electronics in my day, but then, as now, the medical student did not need to know physics to interpret an X-ray picture or an electro-cardiogram (yes we had electro-cardiograms—they date from 1903), any more than the driver of a motor-car needs to take a course in an oil refinery. Now, as then, medical students (except the top five per cent or so) seem to forget most of their physiology and biochemistry during the long vacation which separates the 'pre-clinical' from the 'clinical' part of their course. For this reason, attempts to overlap the two main parts of the course were initiated experimentally in Sheffield in 1920 and are now being used experimentally (though without much success) in some of the more progressive schools of 1970.

Sheffield was in fact a very advanced school of medicine in those days and was one of the first to appoint, in 1920 (in the person of Edward Mellanby), a clinical professor with medical beds and clinical teaching whose background had been medical science rather than medical practice. Apart from his own researches and those of his wife (later Lady Mellanby) his general influence encouraged research in others and an outlook on medicine which was rare in any medical school until twenty-five years later (i.e. after the Second World War).

These innovations and pioneer experiments in Sheffield were due mainly to the foresight of three men, namely Sir Arthur Hall, who was practically the founder of the Sheffield medical school and had a genius for finding, persuading and appointing the right men to take charge of the new department, J. B. Leathes, who was one of these men, a physiologist of international reputation, and Dr A. E. Barnes, whose outlook was well ahead of his time, and who inspired us to hold a healthy and sceptical attitude to most of the remedies then in use, and a disbelief in any dogmatic statement not supported by evidence. These and others of nearly equal calibre were my teachers and I owe them a real debt of gratitude. Furthermore, in those days when success was earned by competition in private practice, Barnes was generous in the extreme and did all he could to help and encourage a much younger man, although in a sense he was bound to become a rival.

Since those days, medicine, especially with the advent of the full-time professors and university departments of medicine, has become a more academic subject of study than it was in former years, and this, along with other topics briefly discussed here, will come in for further consideration later.

The advent of the psychiatrist into the general hospital is perhaps one of the things which merits the title of a real innovation in medical education, and of course the qualifications for entry into medicine have changed along with the general expansion of universities and the greatly increased demands for higher education.

In 1920, as now, the organization of medical practice was changing with the development of specialization. General practitioners complained that they were being isolated from the teaching hospitals and that the medical course was an inadequate preparation for the true practice of medicine. The practical doctors said we were teaching too much science, and the scientists said we were teaching too little.

Postgraduate medical education, on the other hand, has changed out of recognition, not only in the training of specialists, which has long been on a fairly satisfactory, if unorganized apprentice basis, but because until 1953 there was no compulsory period of postgraduate training under supervision and a new graduate could go straight into general practice the day after his qualification. The speed with which newly found facts, new methods and new treatments now establish themselves in medicine is such that all doctors today accept and acknowledge the need for continuing education at all stages of their career. Partly because of this and partly because of the just demands of a more educated society, there is no doubt at all that standards of general practice have improved enormously.

Above all, patients have changed. The poor, underfed, underclad, dirty, ignorant and ill-informed people, silent and undemanding, who used to wait indefinitely in the out-patient departments of my student days have been replaced by a less needy and more aware generation who rightly demand higher standards of treatment and respect. Unfortunately they do not always get them. The medical profession is slow to learn that there is no longer a hospital class who are tacitly prepared to await the doctor's convenience.

Apart from the changes in social conditions, the pattern of disease has changed and, because of new methods of investigation, many patients are now admitted for diagnosis rather than for treatment and so are not in need of intensive nursing care. With these changes comes the need for a different type of hospital, a need as yet far from being fully met. Buildings of a past century are inadequate in comfort, in privacy, in laboratory and X-ray accommodation and (if teaching hospitals) in space for students and their teaching needs. Accommodation for patients who need not be confined to bed is usually quite inadequate.

The students themselves, I should say, have not changed very much. It is still just as depressing to find out at the final examination how little some of them seem to know of the most elementary facts after five or six years of study, and just as rewarding to listen with amazement and humility to the mature judgment and knowledge of the few who are really outstanding.

As for the teachers, they too are the same mixture, the few brilliant intellects, the exhibitionists, the less-than-adequate. The courteous ones who seem to love seeing patients, and the discourteous who seem to hate them. The great medical personalities, some say, have died out and to some extent this is true. Medicine is far less a matter of opinion than it once was, and far more a matter of findings which can be put to the test in the laboratory or the X-ray department, and proved right or wrong. To put forward one's opinion with sufficient conviction required a little of the histrionic talent. Wisdom, knowledge and experience were essentials but in themselves not quite enough. Medicine today is much more a matter of team-work and success depends much less on rivalry. The forceful histrionic personalities are not so much at home in the atmosphere of the specialized academic department of today where the reputations of modern medicine are mostly built, or maybe it is the humility required of the true scientist which is incompatible with the development of this type of personality. Perhaps this, after all, is the most radical change in medical teaching since my student days.

3. The Practice of Medicine

The late Sir James Spence once said 'The real work of a doctor is not an affair of health centres or public clinics or operating theatres or laboratories or hospital beds.... The essential unit of medical practice is the occasion when in the intimacy of the consulting room or the sick room a person who is ill, or believes himself to be ill, seeks the advice of a doctor whom he trusts. This is a consultation and all else in the practice of medicine derives from it.' Thus spoke a great clinician. I would go further in one respect and say that, to the physician, consultation is not only his real work but it is also his real fulfilment, and this is why I look upon my first twenty years in medicine as the most satisfying time of my life from the point of view of the practice of medicine: it was during these years that, after working as a hospital resident (for which I was paid £50 per annum) and later as a junior in university departments (with a salary of £250 per annum on which Margaret and I married), I was appointed a Registrar in Medicine, and finally, to my great pride, in 1931, Physician to the Royal Infirmary, Sheffield.

In those days such an appointment was honorary and you had to make your living in private practice. There were some lean years, for I had no inherited wealth, but my father was able to guarantee an overdraft for me so that I could live in a house big enough to hold a consulting room, and buy a motor-car. But then success came rather suddenly and when I left to join the army in 1941 I relinquished a very considerable consulting practice.

To return to James Spence, who makes many points with considerable economy of words: he said, for instance, that the true consultation is an intimate affair between doctor and patient; that the doctor should be someone whom the patient trusts; that the patient who believes himself to be ill is just as properly the subject of a consultation as the one who really is ill; and lastly that 'all else in the practice of medicine derives from it'. Here he tells us in a few words that the true *raison d'être* of the whole edifice of the modern hospital with its laboratories, its X-ray departments, its clinics, its operating theatres, derives from this essential unit of medical practice, the occasion of the consultation.

I knew Spence well, and all who knew him respected him for his wisdom and humanity. He was not only a good clinician with his patients, most of whom in his later years were children, but also a good enough clinician to realize that a lump in his own neck was a manifestation of lung cancer which was shortly to cause his death. He spent the last few months cheerfully continuing to work but gradually handing on his responsibilities to others.

By consultation he would, of course, include the first interview between the patient and his own family doctor, but wherever it takes place there must be the necessary time and privacy for intimate information to be exchanged. Only thus can the real facts gradually emerge and they are not always what they seem to be. Sometimes only a time-consuming appraisal of the whole of the circumstances and the patient's personality will lead you to a diagnosis. The person who makes light of a trivial disturbance of the bowels may really be concealing a dread of internal cancer. Perhaps he has cancer but, whether he has or he has not, a three-minute interview and the prescription of some pills will do him no good.

Some illnesses are patently psychological in origin, or at least have strong emotional factors in their causation, but even the clearest cases of serious organic disease contain an important emotional content, and their outcome may be determined by the attitude of the patient to the illness. Complete devotion to science in medicine is unnecessary in many cases, impossible in most, and can quite easily be mischievous.

Consider a woman who has found a lump in her breast and who at once thinks of a friend who found something similar and was dead within a year, or of a close relative who died after several years of suffering. According to her nature and the kind of reception she has learnt to expect from her doctor, she may rush to him at once or may continually evade the encounter lest her worst fears be confirmed. Whether she comes early or late the doctor should surely gain insight into her mind as well as her body: *Guérir quelquefois, soulager souvent, consoler toujours.**

Quote

Or take for example a disease in which medical science has been very successful, namely diabetes. It needs control by diet and often by insulin injections. It may need admission to hospital while the correct regime is worked out. The future fate of the patient depends, however, not merely on his observing dietary rules and insulin injections, but also on his personality and that of his wife. In two such patients almost indistinguishable from a scientific point of view, the one probably aided and abetted by his wife, will give up most of his useful work and become a neurotic invalid dominated by the ritual of insulin injections, sterilization of syringes and calculation of the amount of protein, carbohydrate and fat which can be consumed at any meal, provided of course that the food is carefully weighed. The other patient accepts the routine, choosing his food by reasonably informed guesswork from the menu available in the hotel where he happens to be staying and injecting his insulin if necessary in the lavatory adjoining the Boardroom, or even into his leg under the dining-table; in fact, looking upon the whole thing, once he has been educated to understand it, as a rather annoying but occasionally amusing inconvenience.

The enormous battery and frightening possibilities of modern investigation can never replace the initial consultation which is the all important preliminary to the use of scientific methods of investigation which may come later. Neglect of care and thoroughness at the beginning results in a great deal of bad pseudo-scientific medicine and unnecessary investigation which may lead only to false clues; and this occurs every day in the

---

* To cure sometimes, to relieve often, to comfort always.

sophisticated atmosphere of the hospitals of Europe and America and other highly developed parts of the world.

To interpret the results of his examination the doctor must have a profound knowledge of disease and of the basic scientific principles which are necessary to understand it. He must keep this knowledge constantly up to date. But the preliminary assessment of the diagnostic possibilities stems from the unique qualities of the human mind which is able to take in a very large number of data, to sift their relative significance in an incredibly short time, and to recognize therefrom a pattern which fits closely enough to what has been seen before, or to what has been learnt about the behaviour of various states of ill-health. It is a skill more closely allied to the skill of the connoisseur examining a picture or an old Italian violin than it is to what we normally think of as science, and it is a skill which is in danger of being neglected so long as medical students are mainly taught by medical scientists in hospital, who only see patients already selected for hospital treatment, who have all the resources of investigation at their immediate command, and who shut their eyes to the enormous extent of ignorance which still remains. Ask a medical scientist to explain hunger to you, or anorexia (which is the opposite) or tiredness, and you will soon find how ignorant we still are of basic physiology.

Of course the enormous developments in medical science which *have* taken place have altered the pattern of disease. Pulmonary tuberculosis in a young person in this country is now so unusual that it is no longer a diagnosis which immediately comes to mind. Pneumonia, formerly a killing disease in young persons, has become almost trivial and fatal septicaemia from boils and septic injuries is almost unknown. The age range of patients in the medical wards of a modern hospital is very different from what it used to be. Most of them are over fifty, many of them sixty and seventy. Coronary heart disease, cancer, and chronic bronchitis are now the killing diseases of middle-age (all of them far commoner in cigarette smokers). Attempted suicide is a much more usual cause of admission to hospital than it used to be.

The modern doctor has a powerful range of remedies at hand, for instance, penicillin and other antibiotics which now control almost all bacterial disease including even typhoid fever, plague and tuberculosis, and the development of diagnostic methods has been an essential accompaniment to modern treatment whether medical or surgical. Modern surgery would be impossible but for the simultaneous development of new anaesthetic methods.

Yet the essential role of the doctor remains in many senses what it has always been. It is still his business to hear what the patient has to say, to examine him and to weigh up the possibilities, and then to give him good advice, whether by prescribing an appropriate remedy, by reassurance, by change of habit or environment, or by reference to hospital for further investigation and treatment. However far the science of medicine and surgery advances, the art of medicine will remain; the art of first identifying the patient's problem (which is something more than merely diagnosing his disease) and the art of applying the science to the needs of the individual patient.

Because of the time, the privacy and the patience which are required in many consultations, it has to be admitted that it is easier to practise the art of medicine at its best under conditions of private practice, and I find this difficult to reconcile with my ardent belief in the Health Service and that Medicine should be available to all without respect to the patient's ability to pay.

It is therefore gratifying to see a great improvement in the service provided for non-paying patients in recent years. Most general practitioners now practise in groups and so can share up-to-date premises where they have an appointments system and the necessary receptionists to work it; and where these conditions obtain there is often a desire on the part of the doctors to practise wholly within the Health Service and not to try to set up two standards. The refusal of successive governments to provide free drugs for private patients together with the high cost of many of the modern antibiotics and other remedies has had its effect in this. And in hospital practice, it is a delight to go into a really modern district hospital with clean light reception areas, an appointments system, and a series of small, but well equipped consulting rooms with adjacent examining rooms where the necessary conditions of privacy can be ensured.

The worst conditions sometimes obtain in the famous teaching hospitals. They are usually in the centre of big towns where land is dear and room for expansion inadequate, so the buildings are often antiquated. Inadequate facilities for teaching lead to the patient being surrounded at intervals by large groups of students, and the devotion of the staff to medical science and research has packed far too much technology into the obsolescent buildings, and requires a staff so large that the patient is lucky if he sees the same doctor twice running. Every possible aid to diagnosis is provided except time and privacy, two of Spence's essentials.

Developments in medical science have also led to a large proportion of the staffs of teaching hospitals working on a fulltime basis and seeing no private patients. What is more important, they have never seen a patient except in a hospital setting. There is no doubt that private practice is a wonderful education to the young consultant; I have never yet met anyone who has done private practice and has not admitted its educative value. As long as the more privileged members of society prefer to have their consultations in private consulting rooms, the doctor who restricts himself to hospital practice tends to cut himself off from the very people who by intelligence or social position are his own equals and superiors. It is still not as easy to treat a barrister as it is to treat a bus-conductor, nor is it as easy to answer his questions, nor will you have in private practice a team of young men ready and anxious to deputize for you, onto whom you can pass a good many of the very things which, inconvenient though they may be, play a major part in making the practice of medicine worthwhile. For instance, talking to the relatives of patients.

Of course, the contrasts are not as clear as they may seem from what I have just written. Conditions in teaching hospitals need not be as bad as this and very often are not. Some are outstanding for their personal care of patients, and just because they take more than their share of very difficult cases which need a highly organized team for their investigation and treatment, they do, of course, take much more of a cross-section of the community than they did forty years ago.

For myself I would gladly pay to have privacy, but not, I hope, to have priority or treatment which others could not afford, though being a senior medical man I cannot avoid having something akin to VIP treatment. Give me a room to myself or put me in a ward with six or twelve or thirty. But not, oh not, in a room for two or three. I would have to be polite to my neighbours and that is asking too much.

To return to the consultation and the practice of medicine: occasionally the physician's most brilliant diagnostic revelations are not as welcome as he expects. Scurvy, for instance, sometimes occurs in old people, especially widowers living alone who have neglected their diet. It often fails to be diagnosed because it is rare enough for any one practitioner to see a case but once in many years. It is, of course, easily curable. But the near relatives may have made up their minds that this is grandpa's terminal illness and they are only calling in a consultant so that their minds can be at rest ('we did everything we could') while they divide the spoils. The news that the illness can be cured in a few weeks may be received with no great enthusiasm. A similar state of affairs often occurs with myxoedema (thyroid deficiency) in elderly patients. The slow deterioration is interpreted as the natural onset of a terminal senility and the dramatic return to normal on appropriate treatment may not give rise to rejoicing.

Patients, I have often said to my students, can be interesting, pleasant, charming, difficult, worrying, exasperating, stupid, but never dull. There is an interaction in all human relationships, and if patients seem dull and unco-operative it is always possible that the fault lies with the doctor. After all, awkward patients are a challenge to professional skill. Nevertheless there seem to be some who by any scoring less than archangelical

29

can at least be considered difficult and it was about one of these, a woman clearly accustomed to getting her own way, that I remember writing one of my more notable letters. It began: 'Dear Dr Johnson, I was interested to see your patient Mrs Freebody. She took great care to tell me how desperately ill she was three years ago when she was under the care of the late Dr Hudson. But I note that it was the doctor who died.'

Complaints by patients in hospital are nearly always genuine, but rarely due to any serious professional mistake; rather are they caused by lack of communication or just lack of thought, understanding and common sense. It is appalling how often patients seem to get pushed around in hospital with no adequate explanation as to what is happening.

If you try to do the best for people in hospital, it is very important to know the appropriate level at which to work. You have a patient about whom you have reason to be anxious who needs the personal skill of one of your radiological colleagues as soon as possible. You meet your colleague in the corridor and detain him for a few minutes while you tell him the story. He promises to arrange an early appointment. Do not think that your duty is now discharged; your friend may continue with the work of the day and forget all about the conversation. The essential next move is to ask Marion to telephone to Bessie and tell her what has been arranged. This ensures—if Bessie knows her stuff—that intention will be translated into action; if not, Marion will be asking why. It is here that hospital communication so often succeeds or fails. The hospital service would do well if it paid distinction awards to secretaries and receptionists. But standards are set at the top; bad chiefs have bad secretaries.

My career as a consulting physician at Sheffield was cut short by the war of 1939-45. Towards the end of the war the new post of full-time Professor of Medicine in the University of Manchester was advertised and, very uncertain as to whether I really wanted to become an academic doctor, I applied. I was, to my surprise appointed. Although this gave me both opportunity and satisfaction, I no longer quite felt myself a real doctor. It was difficult to see any patients without being surrounded by a clutch of students or young medical scientists. Decisions on diagnosis and treatment were more a matter for committee than of personal responsibility. I no longer met the general practitioners and discussed cases with them. Above all I would rather see a patient because somebody wanted my opinion than because the patient was of interest to the teachers and research workers in the department.

The Art of Consultation, which is perhaps the main theme of this chapter reminds me of a story told of Dr Judson Bury who was Physician to the Royal Infirmary, Manchester, from 1889 to 1912 and died in 1944. He was once called to see a wealthy patient who lived in a fine mansion in Derbyshire. The general practitioner in this case had asked him to be particularly tactful in the handling of the relatives. He saw the patient, who was obviously approaching the end of his life, discussed the outlook with the doctor and went downstairs where the relatives were all assembled waiting for the Great Physician's opinion. But the magnificent drawing room was a virtual museum of antique furniture, glass, painting and *objets d'art*. Bury examined them carefully with the eye of a collector and connoisseur, ignoring the presence of the assembled relatives. Suddenly he said to the doctor, 'I suppose there'll be a sale.'

4. The War

I remained in Sheffield for the first two years of the war for I felt that we civilian doctors were as much a part of it as the military ones. No one who experienced the night of the big Sheffield air raid will ever be likely to forget it. This was in December 1940 on a brilliantly moonlit night. I think it went on for five or possibly eight hours. I had been out to a consultation in Attercliffe and the incendiary bombs began to fall as I was driving home.

It was just a month after the famous Coventry raid. The Sheffield one was never publicized because by then it was deemed inadvisable to give the Germans any information as to the effects of the raids. The attack was directed almost entirely to the central part of the town and large areas of shops were destroyed. Although numerous bombs came whistling down, the greater damage was done by fire. I was living in my consulting rooms near the centre of town and the house exactly opposite, where some of my colleagues had their rooms, was burnt to the ground.

Altogether, we had incendiaries on our house on three separate occasions. My secretary (Marion) and I used to go around putting them out or pushing them off the roofs of neighbouring houses. We had organized a fire-watching and fire-fighting service with our neighbours. There was also, of course, a duty roster amongst the physicians and surgeons at the Royal Infirmary, but the night of the big raid was not one of my nights on duty. When the raid began to abate we tried to get some sleep in the cellar where we had some bunks. As it was also the wine cellar the night was not spent wholly in a state of terrified apprehension. There were seven of us, Marion, two friends of hers, two housemaids and myself, and an amiable but

frightened Frenchwoman who came to the door some time
during the raid to seek shelter. I shared a bunk with one of the
housemaids. She was rather a heavy girl and, the bunks being
narrow and perhaps for other reasons, we shared it head to
tail.

When the bombing period subsided in 1941, I began to become disenchanted with the civilian life and, as in 1917, felt the
urge to join my colleagues in the forces. I served for a year in
a military hospital in Chester, but it seemed to me that I had
been doing better work in civilian life than supervising the
treatment of young soldiers, many of whose symptoms were
more closely related to a distaste for army life than to any
known pattern of disease. So I began to pull strings for a posting abroad, for being already forty-two I feared that they were
planning to keep me on home duties.

I was posted to a military hospital which was mobilizing in
Scotland. We sailed in a large convoy from the Clyde in February 1943, through the Bay of Biscay, past the Straits of
Gibraltar, right into the Mediterranean at the time when the
whole of the French coast was controlled by the Germans, and
landed at Algiers. The convoy ahead of us had been bombed
and several ships sunk, and the convoy which followed us met
a similar fate. We were menaced by enemy aircraft which
seemed, however, to be more observatory than actually aggressive. A good deal of anti-aircraft fire went up and there was the
ever-present danger of submarine attack, which seemed to be
much more frightening at three o'clock in the morning than it
was during the bright daylight.

The weather in the Bay of Biscay was particularly bad. Fortunately I do not suffer from sea-sickness and in a ship which
was absolutely packed with officers and men I was one of the
very few who were not affected. On the worst day I think there
were only six of us in the Officers' Quarters at lunch and I
remember that we had roast pork and apple sauce. Playing
bridge was difficult. The cards would suddenly slide across the
table and the deal would have to be repeated but this was
rather useless because your partner, or one of your opponents,

would suddenly turn green and disappear and the game had to be abandoned.

We landed at Algiers and for several weeks had to wait there for our equipment which was coming on a slower convoy. This was a very trying time for the morale of our hospital staff who had literally nothing to do. We were tented, of course, and sleeping on the bare ground where there were brightly striped caterpillars six inches long and occasional scorpions.

Our camp was on a hill above Algiers; we would sometimes go down into the town during the day and walk back in the evening. I made friends with some French families during this time and discovered a French woman who spoke Italian but practically no English. Being convinced that after Africa we should go on to Italy, I arranged to have Italian lessons with her and can confirm what I had several times been told—that it is good to learn a foreign language through the medium of another foreign language; it prevents you forming the bad habit of translating everything into English. As any necessary explanations were given in French moreover, I was having two lessons for the price of one.

One of my more unpleasant experiences during that time occurred one evening when I was walking back to Spur Camp and lost my way. The sub-tropical night falls fast and suddenly, and darkness was overtaking me. I came to a farmhouse and on entering it found a French woman to whom I told my plight in my extremely bad French. Yes indeed, she knew Spur Camp but it was a little difficult to find from here especially as it was getting dark. She was about to attempt an explanation of the route when a couple of Arabs appeared and seemed to be going in the right direction. She asked them if they spoke French and they did. She explained that I wanted to find Spur Camp and they said they would take me. So we set out together. By now it was quite dark and they seemed to prefer to walk one on either side of me. Although they knew that I had some knowledge of the French language, which they had spoken quite fluently not long before, they now spoke only Arabic to each other and, of course, I had not the slightest idea what they were saying.

They were both tall men and could almost talk to each other over my head. Perhaps they were talking to see if I understood, but it seemed to me at the time much more likely that they were discussing just where they would take me to rob me and make an end of me, or worse! British soldiery of the First Army had not long been in Algiers. It was known that the natives had not been friendly and there were horrifying stories about of British soldiers who had been found stabbed or mutilated. The removal of the male genital organs as part of this mutilation had been a theme in these stories that had recurred more than once.

This I think is the most frightening experience in my memory. I do not know to this day whether the intentions of those Arabs were wholly amiable or whether they were in fact discussing the best way of disposing of me, but if they were friendly they could surely have made at least some attempt to say a few words of conversation in a common language. I wondered if they realized that I was in the Medical Corps and therefore unarmed; in any case two large men armed with knives could have quickly made short work of one who threatened them with a revolver. Nevertheless I put my right hand in my pocket and kept it there as if to pretend that I was in fact armed.

As this is autobiographical the reader will, of course, realize that I survived. We walked on for what seemed to be an interminable time but was probably only ten or fifteen minutes, during which they spoke almost continuously to each other in that guttural Arabic which I quickly learned to dislike. But this was not to be cold-blooded murder: quite suddenly the lights of a lorry came round a bend—a British army lorry. My only fear now was that it would drive past. I was in uniform, and a Lieutenant-Colonel at that, and I stepped out into the road making gestures for the lorry to stop, which it promptly did. I asked if they could take me to Spur Camp, which they could. With at last a smile on my face, and in my very best French, I profusely thanked my two good friends who had been so kind as to put me on the right road.

In Algiers I came to know some of the civilian hospital doctors and was introduced to typhus fever, in those days endemic in Algeria. They were surprised that a doctor of my experience had never seen typhus before. Like many so-called tropical diseases it really depends not on temperature but on dirt, squalor and bad hygiene, for it is carried by lice (only the body-louse by the way, not the head-louse or the 'crab-louse'). It was, of course, common in England where it was sometimes known as jail fever, and especially in Ireland. In Algiers it was prone to occur mainly in the winter months when, in the cold nights, people tend to huddle together in close quarters. Doctors are at risk through visiting patients and I was told that six or seven of them had died during an epidemic of the previous winter.

Although the weeks spent in Algiers were chiefly notable for boredom, frustration, impatience and discomfort, when our equipment at last arrived I was sorry to leave my French friends. The equipment, 180 tons of it, was loaded directly into trucks at the docks, and left by rail for our unknown destination accompanied by a small party with an officer in charge. The Commanding Officer of the hospital then went off to reconnoitre the new site which was said to be near Bône, about 400 miles to the east, and I was left to take charge of the remaining 108 officers and other ranks who were to travel by ambulance train. At dawn on the appointed day my party was packed up and ready to be driven to the station in lorry-loads (ourselves and three tons of baggage), but the lorries did not appear. I ascertained by telephone that they had in fact left at the correct time. When eventually they arrived it turned out that the leading driver did not know his way to the camp and had been given a map reference but no map.

We went first to Rouiba, some ten miles away, where an enormous hospital train—actually two trains joined together—was waiting. There were a few corridor coaches but the rest of the train consisted of luggage vans and horse-wagons which had been converted to take stretchers. The two officers in charge of the train were not expecting us. The Railway Transport Officer (R.T.O.) turned up later and did know that we were joining the train, but did not know where we were going. Neither, I discovered by personal enquiry, did the engine drivers, except that we should go in an easterly direction.

Eventually we set out. We stopped at every station for 400 miles. This was probably because the track, except at the stations, was mostly single, and we had to give other trains the opportunity of passing. No passenger ever got in or out and some of the stations seemed to be in remote unpopulated districts.

The train was crowded with personnel and kit, water was short and the latrine accommodation appalling. The ancient engines (two of them) clanked and groaned and exhaled steam at every crack and orifice. Once we failed on a gradient and the engine-drivers backed the long train down the hill again, paused to get up more steam, tried the hill again with a rush, and just made it. After some days we reached Guelma where several trains were held up because parachutists had blown up the line ahead. I wanted to let the men wander into the town for exercise and a change of scene but was told by the R.T.O. that according to his information the train 'might leave at any minute in the next twenty-four hours'. He also had no information as to our destination.

After twenty-seven hours we left for Duvivier where we detrained with all our baggage and got into an enormous goods train hauled by an electric engine. At Mendovi the R.T.O. was actually expecting us and we detrained again and went on by lorry to Zerizer near Bône. There we met the baggage party who had already arrived and had only lost one or two trucks in spite of the tendency of the French railwaymen to split up and re-shunt the train at every available marshalling yard. This party had travelled via Bône where they were held up by an air raid. The officer in charge, solicitous for the safety of his men, had made them take shelter under some railway wagons in the siding; only later did they discover that the wagons were full of ammunition.

We put up our tented hospital and were receiving patients within a week, but after fourteen days we had orders to pack up and move on to Oued Zarga. We never had time to set up there because events in the First Army were moving fast, so we went forward to Medjes el Bab. Here we received a hundred patients within twelve hours of our arrival. Conditions were primitive and chaotic. Lorry loads of prisoners were arriving all day long in the nearby prison camp, many of the German officers driving their own vehicles without escort and even stopping to ask the military police the way to the camp. One of them picked up three Americans who had been injured by a mine and brought them to our hospital. He said we could keep his vehicle if we took him on to the camp, which we obligingly did. It was a converted eight-cylinder Horch which I drove many times though always with sandbags under the seats because the verges of the roads were mined; everyone manoeuvred for a position as near as possible to the centre of the road.

After only nine hectic days at Medjes, during which we had at one time French, Germans, Italians, British, Americans and Arabs all in the same ward, we moved on again even before we had completed setting up the hospital. This time it was to a site near Tunis, for the North African campaign was over.

In Tunis, as before, everything was in chaos. The hospital was hastily erected. The heat was intense. The engineers brought piped water to our tented wards but in their haste did not sink the pipes, so that in the hot afternoon sun the water from the 'cold' tap was too hot to wash in. The temperature in my tent one day was 120° F; if you walked across to the wards sweat ran down your legs. Flies were so plentiful that you ate your food with one hand, flicking them away with the other.

The whole British, German, French, American and Italian forces now seemed to be suffering from bacillary dysentery. At one time almost the entire medical staff except myself went down with it. Just how I escaped I do not know. It just shows that health and strength are two different things, for I was at least ten years older than most of my staff and patients and had never taken any trouble to keep fit; I never noticed that the Commandos who had been trained to the utmost of physical strength showed any more immunity from malaria, dysentery or hepatitis than the rest of us.

During the whole of this time we had no female nursing staff as the women had not yet been sent to the forward areas. We simply had ward orderlies and staff sergeants, some of them splendid and properly trained in the regular or territorial R.A.M.C. Others had come from a mixed background of civilian jobs and had received a minimum of instruction.

We had no deaths from dysentery, mainly because the usual forms of bacillary dysentery although very discomforting and temporarily disabling are usually self-limiting and not dangerous to otherwise healthy young men, and also because we had supplies of various sulphonamide drugs. The supplies of these were inadequate, however, which gave me the excellent opportunity of comparing the progress of those who had the drug with those who had the usual pre-sulphonamide regime. (I always had some sulphonamide in reserve in case any patient appeared to be taking a potentially dangerous course.) The ward sergeant and I recorded the duration of temperature elevation, diarrhoea, passage of blood and other symptoms and I later published the results. There was no doubt of the efficacy of the sulphonamides in limiting the duration of illness and incapacity. The occasions must be rare, I reflected, in which within a week or ten days one can make a controlled experiment on some hundreds of cases, and make use of the golden opportunity of inadequacy of supply so that one's conscience is quite clear in withholding treatment from more than half the cases. There was one unexpected snag: the pocket notebooks in which we wrote our brief records were so soaked in sweat that the ink was barely legible.

After dysentery there followed a major epidemic of infective hepatitis (jaundice) and then, in the appropriate season, malaria. This period of my service in North Africa lasted for about a year before we moved on to Italy.

It must not be supposed that my military career consisted of an unblemished record of unsparing service to King and Army, for I was in fact very nearly arrested on a charge of mutiny—

one of the most serious of military crimes. I was, at the time, in charge of the Medical Division of a military hospital and a friend of mine was in charge of the Surgical Division. We were temporarily under a Commanding Officer not, in our estimation, equal to his task. Of course we temporary soldiers did not know the regulations as well as we might have done, but we decided (after reading the relevant sections of King's Regs) that we could seek an interview with the D.D.M.S.* and report to him the state of the unit and the shortcomings of its Commanding Officer, provided we notified the C.O. himself of our intentions. We did so, and he accepted the situation and passed on our complaint. However, he proceeded to report us to Headquarters with a view to charging us with mutiny, in the sense that two or more persons had conspired together to overthrow authority.

I admit I am still as ignorant of the regulations as I was then, but I am not sure that a charge of mutiny can be sustained if the persons concerned have given proper notice of their intentions. There were some people at Headquarters, however, who evidently were not blind to the situation and had some appreciation of the good work which I honestly think the medical staff were doing. Nevertheless I guess that the Headquarters staff, who of course appealed to the War Office for advice, had to plan a series of actions which looked as if some disciplinary measure was being taken. The charge of mutiny was not proceeded with. The C.O. went home, and I was posted to another hospital— twice the size of the one I had left.

My new C.O. was excellent, a territorial who was normally in medical practice in the North of England. It was in this hospital that I did most of my most satisfying medical work in North Africa. I became good friends with the C.O. and on one occasion, after we had moved to Naples and our work in Africa was over, I asked for the loan of his typewriter (I was writing something for our hospital magazine, a cyclostyled production which was circulated at approximately monthly intervals). He lent me his typewriter and with it a piece of carbon paper which had evidently been used only once before. The message on it was

* Deputy Director of Medical Services.

clearly legible and, starting as it did with my name, I proceeded to read it through. It was a citation for onward transmission to the War Office, recommending me for the O.B.E. This, of course, did not succeed. The mutiny episode had really been treated very sympathetically, leading to my promotion to a bigger hospital and not interfering with my later promotion to be Consulting Physician to Southern Army, India. But to give me a decoration as well, I heard later through devious channels, was going a bit too far for an officer whose record contained a charge of mutiny. It never even occurred to me to wonder why the C.O.'s recommendation, which by such a peculiar chance had fallen into my hands, had not succeeded; there must have been plenty of more deserving people.

In February 1944 we moved across to Naples to occupy and set up our hospital in a large technical school. The Italian winter does not last long but can be intense and there was snow on Vesuvius when we arrived in the Bay of Naples. This was all very beautiful, but as all the windows of the school had been smashed by air raids, our first days in Naples were bitterly cold.

The city was in very bad shape: the natives, practically starving, would steal food from our swill bins. They were living underground in cellars in conditions of indescribable squalor and the typhus epidemic was just subsiding. Nevertheless the atmosphere of Naples and Italy made itself clear even on our first arrival. We marched up from the docks and the disciplined, beautiful and harmonious singing of our Italian prisoners on that march was in sharp contrast to the raucous and bawdy efforts of the British soldiery (none of the Italian prisoners defaulted—why I don't know; probably most of them didn't live in Naples) and my memories of subsequent wanderings through the streets of Naples, squalid, dirty and unkempt as they were, are of graceful Italian women hanging washing from third- or fourth-storey windows, singing arias from Italian opera.

One evening when our hospital was fully operative we suffered a bombing raid and had to go through the usual drill of getting the patients down to the lower parts of the hospital, taking special care of those who were mentally disturbed. Of course, in any air raid you never know where the next bomb is going to fall, but this was not a particularly frightening one, and, when it was all over and the patients were restored to their normal quarters, I went to the Officers' ward to have a cup of tea with the night sister. While we were sitting and drinking our tea together, the whole of this great concrete building began to vibrate as if some giant had taken hold of it and shaken it from its foundations. It was an earthquake, but fortunately a very minor one, which altogether lasted less than a minute. Nevertheless it seemed to have some superhuman quality about it which made it far more frightening than the air raid which had preceded it.

Later, in March 1944, when still in this hospital, we were to witness the biggest eruption of Vesuvius for two hundred years. It was one of the greatest sights of my life (the others I think being the Taj Mahal and the Victoria Falls). Seen at night from the windows of our hospital it was superb. Fortunately the wind was blowing in the right direction (for us) but the ash was falling so fast on the roof of the military hospital at Pompeii that it had to be evacuated for fear of a recurrence of the historic destruction of that town (which was by ash and not by lava). Flames shot up thousands of feet into the sky and a huge stream of lava came down the mountainside slowly, like treacle spilling over from a tin. The main lava stream was thirty feet deep and half a mile wide. It glowed bright red in the night and ran through a number of villages, but the warning system was such that I think no one was injured.

This went on for several days; I remember coming back to Naples from Rome about four months later to see my old friends, and by now you could walk across the lava stream, but if you took a stick and scraped into the surface of the lava it was still hot enough to light a piece of paper. A little Italian boy came with us and at one point there was some masonry sticking up through the lava. This was in the village where he had lived. 'Scuola finita' he said with obvious relish.

Before I left Naples for Rome I had the good fortune to have a rather serious frontal sinusitis which, when the acute symptoms had subsided, necessitated a short period of convalescence, spent on the beautiful island of Ischia. But my enjoyment of the beauties of Ischia was alas overlaid by anxieties for my son who was in gunboats in the Channel, and this was the time of D-Day. Fortunately he survived the war with no more than a tiny piece of shrapnel through the lobe of one of his ears. As he has rather big ears his friends treated it as a great joke, implying that no one with normally disciplined ears would have been hit in this way.

I reached Rome just after the Allied occupation, but stayed only a few weeks before my posting to Southern India. In Rome, as in Naples, opera went on throughout the war. There was much to do and see, but little time in which to do it. A friend of mine came with me to St Peter's and the Sistine Chapel which, like the Taj Mahal, is one of those things you have heard about so often that, until you actually see it, you cannot believe that its beauty lives up to its reputation.

From the Sistine Chapel, by dint of some persuasion in rather bad Italian, we were shown round the Raphael Rooms and the sculpture galleries of the Vatican, which at that time were closed to the public. As we came out we found ourselves mixed up with a long queue of people, and not knowing what we were in for, joined the end. In a short time we were received in audience by the Pope—quite by accident. It was, of course, a public audience, but the colourful ceremony was very impressive—the Swiss Guards in their uniforms, the Pope in white robes carried in on his chair, blessing us and addressing us in Italian, in English and in French, where only a few weeks ago he had, I suppose, been speaking German.

From Rome I was suddenly translated to Southern India to be Consulting Physician to Southern Army with the rank of full Colonel, later Brigadier. Frankly I was disappointed about this, partly because I had learnt to love Italy, and had hoped to see more of Rome and if possible of Northern Italy before the war ended, and partly because in Southern India I was no longer in a theatre of war. The Senior Officers' Mess at Bangalore and the Club of Western India at Poona were conducting their affairs (in 1944) as if the war was an unwelcome intrusion which should not be allowed to disrupt the way of life of the *pukka sahib* and his *mem-sahib*. Somewhat irrationally I resented the comfort, service and food rations which they enjoyed, knowing something as I did of hard work and tinned food that had been my lot in Africa and Italy, and of the short rations of my friends and family in Britain.

It was my job to travel over most of Southern India, visiting our military hospitals, learning something of the Indian way of life and encountering some new diseases including plague, which I was able to see in the plague hospitals of Poona and Bangalore. I may have been the first to use one of the new sulphonamide drugs intravenously in a case of plague, for the military had small supplies not available to all. But plague, like cholera, kills so quickly that early and accurate diagnosis is the first essential, however effective the remedy.

Although we had no plague in the Army it was never very far away. A friend of mine opened a drawer in his desk at Army Headquarters, Bangalore, and found a dead rat in it which had died of plague. The beautiful green-striped bushy-haired tree-rats which chased each other around the roofs were sometimes found dead on the road or in the garden. We did not touch them but poured kerosene over them to kill the fleas, for they had probably died of plague.

The plague bacilli are of course carried by rat-fleas, which are liable to transfer their attentions to the human subject when the rats die off. For this reason it is really quite safe to go around a plague hospital provided that the patients have been rid of their fleas (preferably by someone else) on admission. This does not apply to the deadly pneumonic variety of plague, however, which may be conveyed directly from person to person without the intervention of the flea.

Some day I hope to write the life story of Nathaniel Hodges, the real hero of the Plague of London of 1665. He was a member of the Royal College of Physicians and remained in London when most of the fellows of the college, along with their wealthy clients, had left the city. He describes how he would have a glass of Sack before going out on his rounds into the plague-houses and would burn some paper in the entrance of the house which he thought lessened the danger of contagion (the rat-flea was not then known to be the carrier). He would have more Sack at lunch and again in the evening. He died, poor man, in a debtors' prison. I have often wondered if the alcohol in his blood deterred the fleas from biting him, and also led him into bankruptcy. One day, if there are any fleas left, it would be interesting to plan an experiment to see if a high blood alcohol has any effect on them.

Apart from plague I met all kinds of tropical diseases in India which I had never met before, and many not strictly tropical but due to malnutrition, poverty, ignorance and bad hygiene—florid smallpox in the unvaccinated (a truly loathsome disease), beriberi, leprosy, typhus and malaria again, and diseases due to parasites.

When I returned to England after the war I realized what a minute sample of the problems of world health we sheltered doctors see in this country. Enormous progress has been made in India and other countries since 1945 in nearly all the diseases which were then so common, and while this must in general be ascribed to improved knowledge, to research in chemotherapy, to engineering (the drainage of malarial swamps, for instance) and to the eradication of insect carriers (by D.D.T. and other measures), it may be due in part to the war-time enlightenment of many who, like myself, practised medicine abroad for the first time.

5. Medical Progress

Fifty years ago Medicine was beginning to take on a new look. X-rays, at first used effectively only to show the bones, were finding new applications in the diagnosis of diseases of the chest, heart and stomach. The interpretation of the electro-cardiogram was becoming more refined and had already expanded Sir James Mackenzie's earlier work on irregularities of the heart. Bodily function and its disorders in disease were being explained in physiological and biochemical terms, derived from the work of the great pioneers of physiology such as Claude Bernard, Starling and Bayliss. Micromethods whereby the chemistry of the body could be explored on small samples of blood were being developed. Bacteriology was already well advanced. In brief, physicians were looking into the pathology of the living for confirmation of their diagnosis instead of awaiting the evidence of the post mortem examination.

A healthier attitude of scepticism was developing towards most of the drugs then in use. The few effective medical remedies—such as quinine (in malaria), organic arsenicals (in syphilis) and thyroid extract (in myxoedema) and the pain-relieving opiates—were almost to be counted in single figures, though prevention in a few instances (smallpox, for example, and probably typhoid fever) was possible.

This is why the cure of diabetes and pernicious anaemia in the 1920s was such a dramatic advance to those who remember the medicine of that time. Pernicious anaemia was always fatal before Liver treatment (later liver extract, later Vitamin B12) was developed. Diabetes in its acute, severe form in young people was usually fatal within a few months, or at most two years. Perhaps one should not speak of cure, for this is really replacement therapy; the patient is supplied with the essential substance which he cannot manufacture for himself, the inadequacy of function remains but the deficiency is replaced. The first patient to be treated in Sheffield with insulin was nearly at the last stage of diabetes. His weight was five stone, he was living largely on cabbage. Insulin came just in time, and he lived until 1968.

The major blood groups had been discovered and fatal transfusion reactions could (almost always) be avoided, but it was not until 1935 that Marriott and Kekwick introduced the drip transfusion. This was a major advance in treatment which for some reason is rarely recognized in catalogues of medical progress. The small transfusions usually given before then were not very effective; we used to give a pint of blood from a single donor and the technique was difficult. Often in the 1920s we used the direct method in which donor and recipient lay side by side and a syringeful of blood at a time was taken from the donor and by a two-way tap transferred into the recipient. By turning the tap back again another syringeful was taken from the donor, and so on. I remember transfusing an old lady in a nursing home. We had no blood bank, but a list of volunteer donors. When the donor arrived he had obviously been fortifying himself for the ordeal. We had no breathalysers then but the aroma of alcohol was apparent at some distance. I guess his blood alcohol must have been in the 200 mg range. The old lady was a great worker for the Temperance League. I hastily changed my tactics and did an indirect transfusion, collecting the blood in another room and bringing it to the recipient for infusion (clotting being prevented by the addition of citrate). When we had nearly finished, the old lady said would I thank the dear man who had so kindly given his blood for her, she began to feel better as soon as it started to flow into her veins!

The sulphonamide drugs were the next spectacular advance in medical treatment, in the 1930s. Now that they are largely superseded by the antibiotics it is difficult for anyone qualifying since the war to realize how important they were, for they were the first drugs to be effective in bacterial disease such as pneumonia, septicaemia and cerebro-spinal meningitis, all of which

47

could prove fatal in young persons. I recall a young doctor who was brought into the Royal Infirmary (Sheffield) with an acute staphylococcal septicaemia which developed after he had inadvisedly squeezed a small boil in his nose. He died in five days He was the only child of Scottish parents who had spent most of their savings giving him a medical education. They came down from Scotland, only to see him die. His mother, still steadfast in her simple faith, said to me 'God's ways are no' our ways.'

Then, during the Second World War, came penicillin, the history of which is too well-known to need description. This gave an immediate stimulus to the search for other antibiotics, and later to the development of the semi-synthetic penicillins, so that today we have a whole series of antibiotics effective in boils, in pneumonia, plague, syphilis, gonorrhoea, and most of the bacterial scourges of former years. But not, of course, effective against virus diseases such as the common cold, which remains resolutely incurable and unpreventable.

Of all the post-penicillin antibiotics the most impressive to me is streptomycin because it has (especially when combined with other drugs) practically eradicated pulmonary tuberculosis in young people. This is perhaps the greatest gain of all in my time.

In the same epoch there have been other therapeutic gains; less spectacular because they are concerned with rarer diseases such as adrenal failure, or with the control and amelioration rather than the cure of disease, as in heart failure or high blood pressure. There have also been important gains in diagnosis especially through radiology and biochemistry, without which some of the therapeutic advances could not be used to the full.

It has been a remarkable experience to live through these years of unprecedented medical progress and to be head of a university department of medicine. It was to facilitate the use of scientific methods in clinical medicine (and other clinical subjects) and to stimulate the teaching of science as applied to medicine that these departments were founded, and my own was the first in Manchester. Freed from the cares of private practice, a full-time professor can devote more time to teaching and research but he has a very heavy assignment because, unlike other university professors, he is in charge of the treatment of patients in his unit. However much he may delegate to other competent members of the unit, the final responsibility is one from which he can never escape unless he is absent, and unlike other university professors he has a double dose of committee work, at the hospital as well as the university. This dual responsibility has to be taken into account again when staff are appointed, the qualities of a good doctor and of a good research worker are not always to be found together.

My own interest for many years has been concentrated mainly on the kidney and on high blood pressure which so often accompanies kidney disease. I have been an admirer of the structural beauty and the superb efficiency of the kidney and have conducted a number of investigations which may have added a little here and there to our knowledge of how it carries on its work in health and in disease. The kidney is the guardian of the purity and composition of the blood and responds immediately to all the needs of the moment, conserving when essential body materials are in short supply, removing them when present in excess. Whether we drink little or much, whether we lose salt and water through sweating in the tropics, whether we change our diet every day or every hour, the kidney is equal to its task, and it is essential in the excretion of many poisons (including alcohol!). In my Lumleian Lectures to the Royal College of Physicians I dubbed myself a nephrophile, and the title has stuck.

When the kidney fails any functioning part of the body may be affected. Loss of calcium may soften the bones, so that the patient first appears in the orthopaedic department, or he is sent to an oculist because high blood pressure is destroying the small arteries in his eyes. No wonder that our interests spread from disorders of bone to high blood pressure and to other matters, and in more recent years (after I had left the unit) to dialysis (the so-called kidney machine which does some of the work the kidney would normally be doing) and to renal transplantation. The extraordinary power of adaptation of the normal kidney is such that the layman sounds stupid when he asks if this or that is 'good for the kidneys'. One might as well ask whether walking slowly or quickly is good for the legs. The essence of normal function is that we can face extremes with equal ease. The reader will I hope excuse this little eulogy of a very wonderful and rarely praised organ.

Of course we admitted to the unit medical cases of all kinds which were sent to the hospital, whether for consultation and investigation or as emergencies. We would transfer to other specialists those whose needs were in a branch of medicine in which we did not profess to be expert.

Later I was a member of the Medical Research Council and, later still, Chairman of its Clinical Research Board, and some remarks I have to make on medical research are partly the result of that experience. The object of the Medical Research Council is of course to obtain money from the government and other sources according to the estimated needs and to distribute it within a certain broadly determined policy, preserving as far as possible a balance between free or pure research on the one hand, directed towards new discovery, and applied research on the other hand, directed towards the solving of a specific problem. It is easy to see that the distinction is often difficult to make. Sometimes pure research for its own sake may, quite unexpectedly, throw up the answer to a specific problem, or attempts to cure a disease or symptom may lead to involvement in basic research and discovery. In all research there is bound to be some waste of money. Even Edison said he had spent most of his life inventing things which would not work.

After some fifty years of medical progress it seemed to me reasonable to look at medical research at the present time, and this I attempted to do in my Harveian Oration to the College in 1967 which I called 'Medical Science: Master or Servant?'* One of the striking facts about medical research today is that practically none of the great therapeutic advances has come from practising doctors or departments of clinical research. The anti-

* *The British Medical Journal* 29.11.67, p. 439.

bacterial action of the sulphonamides was wholly worked out in the laboratories of pharmaceutical industry, although the original idea that dyes could be antibacterial stems from that great pioneer explorer of chemotherapy, Paul Ehrlich. From the sulphonamides, chemists have developed other drugs with quite different actions, for instance useful in diabetes and heart failure.

The antibiotics originally sprang from an observation of Pasteur and Joubert in 1867, but Fleming's findings of 1929, which were not developed for ten years, were then taken up by Florey and Chain, who isolated penicillin and demonstrated its effectiveness. Attempts at synthesis were an expensive failure, but better culture methods developed in American Government laboratories and by the Pfizer drug company made penicillin a practical success. From the penicillin idea comes streptomycin, discovered by Waksman and his colleagues in a university department and developed by the Merck drug firm. All the subsequent antibiotics have originated in industrial laboratories, the new penicillins from the Beecham Laboratories.

Poliomyelitis vaccine comes from non-clinical scientists as does insulin, first extracted in a physiology department, one of the few of these therapeutic gains which resulted from good scientific reasoning. Liver treatment of pernicious anaemia did originate in an academic medical unit, but the hard scientific work of discovering its active principle was done in pharmaceutical industry in Britain and the U.S.A. The discovery that cigarette smoking could cause cancer of the lung was due to clinical observation, followed by a first-class study using the techniques of epidemiology.

The synthesis of cortisone was the combined work of an academic non-clinical scientist and a drug firm—namely Merck —done as part of a war-time programme sponsored by the United States Office of Scientific Research and Development. But Hench, of the Mayo Clinic, made a clinical contribution in the application of cortisone in the treatment of rheumatoid arthritis and other diseases.

To continue the recital would be tedious, but the findings are

essentially the same when we look into the origins of anaesthetics, tranquillizers, vitamins, antimalarials, antihistamines,
hypotensives (to reduce blood pressure), sex hormones and oral
contraceptives. Not one originated in a department of academic
medicine or therapeutics. Even D.D.T., so important to preventive medicine, was discovered by Müller, working for the
Geigy company.

The clinicians have exploited the use of the new remedies
and contributed greatly to the development of new diagnostic
methods, and only clinical trials of new drugs on actual patients
can finally decide their value and dangers to man. But the main
concern of the clinical academic departments has been in exploring the mechanisms of disease. While this may sometimes
give rise to clues as to how these mechanisms can be combated,
the kind of experiments carried out on patients in academic
clinical departments are sometimes of more interest to the
doctors than to the patients. Research in surgical departments
has often been of a more practical nature, devising new operations (of which cardiac transplantation is currently the most
publicized) made possible by modern methods of diagnosis,
anaesthesia and antibiotic therapy.

Although I would never suggest that research should be
limited to experiments whose possible benefit can be clearly
foreseen, seven years of service on the Medical Research Council
left me with the conviction that the limited usefulness of many
experiments can in fact be foretold. Many are mere refinements
of measurement, as apparatus becomes more sophisticated and
more expensive, and one can often see in advance that the
experiment can lead only to one of two conclusions, neither of
which is of any great importance. This is what a friend of mine
once referred to as 'squeezing the last drop of blood out of a
foregone conclusion'.

Above all, research should support people with ideas. The
public often seems to think (or to be misled into believing) that
if only there was enough money, the problems of the prevention
and treatment of cancer, leukaemia and heart disease are ready
for solution. But money without ideas only leads to a lot of

people being supported on reasonably adequate incomes, going over the same ground with a few new tools. Research without ideas is sterile, ideas without money are aborted. But given a really new principle deriving from one enlightened person, or a small team of enlightened workers, a lot of comparatively routine research suddenly becomes worth supporting, and at this stage a great deal of money and men may be usefully employed, before the new seam is fully worked out. Witness the widespread search for new antibiotics which followed the initial discovery of penicillin and which led to the discovery of the tetracyclines, and of streptomycin and the cure of pulmonary tuberculosis. It is at this age that the closest collaboration between research departments and industry can be most rewarding.

Reluctantly, too, one has to admit that research attracts not only men of vision and originality (of whom there are very few) but also men who find a research career both respectable and escapist and who prefer the shielded academic life to the more difficult task of actually treating patients. Too often do we see a young worker turning out respectable papers in a rather narrow field, in someone else's laboratory. Eventually he gets a Chair in Medicine, and in twenty years' time we find him still studying essentially the same problem. His measurements are more meticulous, and far more expensive, but no new ideas have emerged. Worst of all he has by now brought up a team of younger men still pursuing the same ideas, ploughing the same furrows. This can divert potential research workers into established departments where all the fruitful ideas have already been worked out. Results are certain, and publishable, because there is always something slightly different to measure by new apparatus. Whether it is worth measuring, it is not always welcome to enquire. Carried to its extreme this means that no new subject is ever explored no matter how urgently it needs a new approach.

Psychological medicine for instance tends to be eschewed because 'it is not ripe for development', meaning that no one is putting any new and original ideas into the elucidation of its

53

problems, most of which do not seem to be amenable to the conventional measurements which depend basically on physics and chemistry. Nor will anyone put new ideas into it so long as the lively graduates are all absorbed by the more conventional departments. Of course I overemphasize to make my points, but it is in these tendencies that I see the dangers, and I have had much criticism for calling attention to them, mostly from scientists who preach that we should recognize the limitations of knowledge and be bold in criticism.

Scientific thinking is an essential to the modern practice of medicine and can best be taught in a department where active research is taking place. Medical students should certainly be exposed to this and take part in it as part of their training. But in medicine, unlike pure science, we are concerned also with people, and therefore with human qualities and attitudes towards our work, as well as with ethical considerations which have nothing to do with science. A nice balance must always be maintained while the student is still in his formative years. We must remember that the majority of our students will be, in one way or another, practitioners of medicine rather than scientists and research workers. It may not be good for them to be brought up wholly in units whose first interest is too obviously discovery rather than practice, however well, humanely and expertly the patients in the unit may be treated.

It must further be realized (and this seems particularly hard for university professors to take in) that a doctor in the course of his work needs to know a little of a great many things— for instance, chemistry, physics, biology, psychology, sociology, statistics. He does not have to take them all to degree level.

The young man or woman entering the medical school is likely to have chosen medicine as a career because he or she wants to work with people and has in mind that the cure and relief of suffering should be a rewarding life's work. But academic teachers who do not deign to teach their subject except in depth can have a stultifying effect on youthful enthusiasm and sense of vocation, whether in medicine or any other subject. The student who has chosen literature as his study, inspired

perhaps by Shakespeare's plays, finds himself learning Anglo-
Saxon grammar; the budding musician intent on a career as a
violinist finds himself studying sixteenth-century counterpoint,
and the young theologian, bursting with zeal to serve God finds
that God requires him to read Hebrew and Ancient Greek in
order to communicate. And the young doctor in his early university years is still, in most medical schools, made to study man
as a machine and man as a corpse, but never man as a person,
under teachers who have themselves elected to escape from the
trials, tribulations and rewards of the medical life. By the time
he commences clinical work his youthful enthusiasm may have
left him and he has been conditioned to think of man as a
machine and illness as a defect in the machine which requires
all the resources of modern medical science to detect it and put
it right. One of the duties of his clinical teachers is to give him
a greater understanding of the patient and his attitude to illness,
rather than to consolidate the possible ill-effects of his early
training.

These are difficult matters and were not solved by the Royal
Commission on Medical Education on which I sat for two and
a half years; indeed there can be no ready solution or universal
formula. During our deliberations I was several times told that
all medical education should be 'at university level' but I ven-
tured to put forward my personal belief that to witness the birth
of a baby was an educational experience which no medical
graduate should be without whatever his subsequent choice of
a career might be. But how babies were born at university level
was a question to which I could find no answer, though I
accepted that some of them were conceived on university premises.

An education which fails to harness the interest and enthusiasm of the student from the very first to his life's work is a
bad education whether at university or any other level.

Of course I shall be criticized once again for tilting at the
academics, but can you imagine any organization except a
university which would send doctors into the world without any

sex education of any kind (except purely anatomical or chemical)? For this was the case until quite recently. Like Hans Richter, the conductor, I have put up with criticism before. Richter was born in Hungary and after his initial successes in Austria and in London he came to Manchester where he conducted the Hallé Orchestra from 1897 to 1911. Samuel Langford was the famous music critic of the *Manchester Guardian* (as it then was) during the latter part of this era, and once criticized one of Richter's performances rather harshly. Someone called Richter's attention to it. 'Ah zese critics', said Richter who had never lost his mid-European accent, 'zey are like eunuchs. Zey know all about it but zey cannot do it.'

6. Modern Medicine and how to avoid it

How to be an expert patient

Owing to the claim which dramatic advances in medicine and surgery make upon the public mind there is a tendency to think either that no diagnosis can be made and no treatment carried out efficiently without all the resources of a modern hospital and a team of specialists, or, if the patient seeks the advice of a general practitioner, he expects the doctor to behave like an automatic machine dispensing some new-fangled pill of great efficacy which will at once relieve his symptoms.

These two current attitudes encourage bad doctoring because it is usually easier to act than to think, and so the general practitioner prescribes a pill rather than enquiring more thoroughly into the origins of the patient's complaint, and the specialist finds it easier to order a large number of investigations by X-rays, blood tests and other means, than to indulge in an unhurried interview. Moreover the reactions of the profession (almost automatic in some cases) are conditioned by the fact that the practitioner feels the patient expects him to prescribe, and the specialist feels the patient, having reached this level of demand, expects a full and thorough examination by the kind of techniques which are practised by that specialist. Not necessarily, mind you, by the techniques appropriate to the patient. Thus, if the practitioner sends a patient with backache to a gynaecologist, he will probably find a displacement of the womb, which, of course, he can correct. But the same patient sent to an orthopaedic surgeon or a neuro-surgeon would have investigations directed to the spine, and a genito-urinary surgeon would catheterize the bladder and have X-rays of the kidneys. An osteopath would manipulate the spine which would probably make it either better or worse, or if sent to a psychiatrist, the patient's personality and antecedents would be explored in a series of long and possibly traumatic interviews (exploration of the mind being at least as dangerous as exploration of the body). Possibly the real trouble is the new car, whose seating is not properly adjusted, but no one has the time to unearth as simple an explanation as this.

The layman should realize that most of this is really his own fault. He should train himself to be an expert patient and learn how to conduct himself through illness, which means handling his wife and his doctor. On no account must he tell anyone about his symptoms without giving thought to the consequences, for he has then challenged them and, out of their profound sense of duty, they are bound to take action.

When I was in Sydney in 1964 I was being interviewed by a journalist in an hotel when the telephone rang. I hurried across a highly-polished floor and fell flat on my back, my head hitting the floor with a considerable bang. I picked myself up and answered the telephone. I then noticed that I had a pain in the head and neck and that if I bent my head forwards a tingling sensation passed down both arms. This clearly meant that I had done damage to nerve roots in the spine, and could have indicated a fracture of part of a cervical vertebra. It could have resulted from haemorrhage in the head or neck which would gradually cause unconsciousness or paralysis. On the other hand the betting as usual was in the patient's favour and in all probability the damage was trivial and would gradually right itself.

I was a VIP, about to set out on a tour of Australian medical schools—what should I do? If I reported my symptoms honestly to a medical man, he would be duty-bound at least to see that no serious damage had been done and that I was fit to continue the tour. This would have meant investigations (rather unpleasant ones) in hospital which would probably have laid me out for some days at the very least. They might well have found some minor fracture requiring prolonged rest and other treatment. Clearly I had to make my own decision *prior* to reporting the injury. I decided to tell no one. But the journalist who had witnessed the accident was still present and somewhat concerned about me. I therefore swore him to secrecy but told him that if he heard of my death or serious illness he should report the circumstances of my fall as it might help my widow to claim for compensation. (Actually the tingling of the arms on bending the neck continued for about three months.)

This is a somewhat extreme example and I will give one more. About 1950 I began to suffer from very painful headaches which were so intensified by coughing or laughing that I could hardly bear to do either and had to hold my head in both hands if the urge to cough or laugh was irresistible. My wife thought I should see one of my neuro-surgical colleagues, but I knew that this would lead to tedious and painful investigations and to the cancelling of many appointments. I argued that it was either something that would right itself, or something really serious such as a cerebral tumour. If the latter it would steadily get worse and we could then reconsider the decision. About this time my secretary Marion said, 'It's your sunshine roof.' I had the habit of driving even on quite cold days with the roof of the car open. I shut the roof. The headaches rapidly disappeared.

For these reasons my dictum: 'Never have anything investigated until you know what it is', although said with tongue in cheek, is not quite as stupid as it sounds.

'But,' the layman will say, 'what guidance can you give to us, who are ignorant of the possible significance of our symptoms?' I have given some thought to this problem.

Have a good general practitioner to whom you can talk and in whom you have faith. The best general practitioners realize their important function in protecting the patient from modern medicine (though they may not express it in those words), the worst will put you off with a pill and without an interview, or else send you at once to a specialist (who may be the wrong specialist) without taking time to evaluate your symptoms.

Don't let general practice die out. This would be a tragedy. The general practitioner is *more* necessary in the world of modern techniques and specialization than ever before. His fate is in your hands; the hands of the discriminating public. If you insist on going direct to a specialist on every occasion you will favour the development of the pseudo-specialist who has every gadget at his disposal except wisdom. If you demand nothing but a few pills from your general practitioner, nothing will you surely get. If you insist on having a general practitioner who gives you confidence, consideration and satisfaction, you will help to build up a real élite of general practitioners which is precisely what the public and the profession needs most at the present time. Eventually you may even convince the scientists and academics that the *practice* of medicine at the highest level is the real object of medical education. But my years on the Royal Commission on Medical Education leave me in doubt as to whether this is really possible.

Having got a good general practitioner, here is a list of things which really must be reported, and may require investigation (and possibly treatment) by a specialist equipped with modern diagnostic aids: unexplained or unexpected bleeding from anywhere, e.g. blood in the spit, in the urine, in vomit or from the womb; any ulcer or sore place which fails to heal after a short trial of simple remedies; any lump, especially in the breast, especially if hard; anything affecting the eyes (apart from the slow deterioration of near vision which is natural with age and only requires simple correction with reading glasses); pain in the chest on exertion, or unaccustomed breathlessness; unexplained loss of appetite or loss of weight; abdominal pain if it is severe, persistent or new to you; unexpected irregularity of the bowels in the over-forties; any pain or ulcer in the feet of old people or diabetics; sudden development of thirst; tiredness, which often indicates anaemia or may denote pathological depression, especially in the elderly; severe abdominal pain or earache or headache in children.

The list is not, of course, exhaustive. On the negative side I would say: do not demand relief by medication for symptoms which common sense and experience tell you will right themselves in a few days, for instance, trivial headache and backache, mild gastric and bowel symptoms, and the common cold.

Over-prescribing

Two of the current defects of the medical profession are over-prescribing and over-investigating. Although the doctors are largely to blame, these also partly result from the demands of patients.

Now that I have given up the active practice of medicine, I am sometimes called upon to be a member of a Medical Appeal Tribunal as set up under the Industrial Injuries Act. Many of the people whom we see are suffering from various degrees of backache and in most such cases one would think, from their demeanour and the ease with which they walk around, that the pain is really quite bearable provided they avoid the kind of strain and the kind of movement liable to bring it on. Although the symptoms are intermittent many of these people are taking a dozen or more pills every day and two or three different ones at night. As most of the pills are given with a view to alleviating the backache and ensuring a night's rest they are pills of an analgesic (i.e. pain-relieving) and sedative nature liable to cause inertia, depression and, in large quantities, even mental confusion.

Because of the development of these symptoms, the patient is sent to see a psychiatrist who now prescribes anti-depressive pills to counteract the depressing pain-relieving ones. Many of the patients would be much better off if they took no pills at all, and of course the psychological effect of taking perhaps three different pills every four hours can itself be harmful and confirm in the patient's mind the idea that his back will never recover and that he will be disabled for the rest of his life.

Let me make it clear that I am not denying that these people have a true disability and am not unsympathetic to their genuine claims, for many can only find employment in heavy occupations which would be detrimental. What I am saying is that intermittent pain, which can be prevented by avoiding those actions and positions which induce it, does not require the hourly administration of undesirable drugs.

In 196: I developed a pain in the right side. It was never severe and most of the day when I was at work I did not think of it at all. But if I did think of it, there it was, and it was especially noticeable during the night. It was still constant but never severe and it was difficult to say whether I woke up and noticed the pain or whether it was the pain that woke me. Because of its nature, its situation and its constancy I thought it was probably something unimportant such as a minor involvement of one of the intercostal nerves at its exit from the spinal column (for I had often had backache and I knew that my spine was more than sixty years old). The other alternative seemed to me to be cancer of the liver and so I palpated my abdomen from time to time to see if my liver was enlarging, but it was not. Had it been cancer of the liver there was nothing whatever to be done about it, so lost time was of no particular importance. Eventually I decided to have an X-ray and a peculiar thing was found, namely a lump in one of my ribs. We thought we had better have a look at it to make sure that it was not malignant and two surgical friends of mine operated and removed the rib and the lump (which turned out to be non-malignant) and also removed the pain.

Come to think of it, this is the oldest operation ever recorded (see Genesis 2:21). But my surgeon wasn't God (though there are some surgeons who seem to think they are), and it was not God but the anaesthetist who 'caused a deep sleep to fall upon Adam', and the rib removed did not alas turn miraculously into a beautiful woman. Because one's mind even under such mild provocation can become unable to concentrate on heavy literature, I took into hospital some miniature scores of string quartets and was mentally listening to the slow movement of the Brahms A minor when they came to transport me to the operating theatre. The melody was still running through my head when I came round. (Triumph of Brahms over Halothane.)

Of course, it was very painful to move during the day or two after the operation, but in accordance with modern custom I was encouraged, or rather helped, to get out of bed on the second day, and provided you stayed in the right position there was really no pain that any person of reasonable stamina could not quite easily put up with. I was in the orthopaedic and casualty ward which is, of course, noisy with emergency admissions all night. The worst noise is the suction apparatus used to clear the respiratory passages of the seriously injured and unconscious patients. I was told that I could have an injection of morphine at any time if I needed it and sleeping tablets were prescribed to ensure that I got a night's rest.

I refused to take either for very good reasons. The diagnosis was now made and it was (correctly) assumed that there would be no more trouble with the lump in the rib. It therefore seemed to me that I faced only two more dangers. One was thrombosis in the deep veins of the legs with the possibility of embolus into the lungs which could, of course, be fatal. In layman's terms it means that if you lie inert after an operation which has diminished your mobility the blood may clot in the veins of your legs and a big clot may suddenly become dislodged and block up the main arteries to the lungs.

My only other danger was a condition known as collapse of the lung, which is liable to occur after operations when the patients find it difficult and painful to cough and secretions which would normally be coughed out tend to accumulate and block the smaller bronchial passages. These, then, were my two dangers. The first of these would be greatly increased if I were heavily sedated so that I lay immobile all night. The second danger would be greatly increased if I had drugs like morphine which lower the threshold of the cough reflex. So the two drugs which my surgical advisers were ready to prescribe as a routine measure seemed to me to be the very two which ought to be avoided. (Of course, if it had turned out to be a bigger and more serious operation with a great deal of pain, the arguments could have been different, and I am by no means asserting that no patient should have sedation after an operation.) I argued further that, having nothing whatever to do the following day, sleep was a luxury but not a necessity. Marion filled my small flask with sherry each day and smuggled it into my bed-cupboard.

In fact I got a good deal of sleep. I moved my legs about

regularly every time I was awake and I deliberately took deep, slow breaths, so that the air passages would not get clogged up. The night-nurse was a congenial person rather like Gracie Fields. I was in a room to myself and about three in the morning when the ward was quieter she would come in and tell me funny stories.

I suppose if there is a moral to be drawn, it is that doctors should think before they prescribe and that patients should think before they take the drugs which the doctors prescribe.

Over-investigation

Over-investigation has already been obliquely referred to in this chapter in considering the possible consequences to the patient of reporting symptoms either to his wife or his doctor. In fact the consequences of over-investigation can be quite serious.

A consultation followed by the necessary investigations at the right time and with a specific objective in view may be salutary at the least, life-saving at the best, and a preventive of morbid and chronic introspection. A consultation leading only to delays and uncertainties may be a powerful incentive to the invalid life.

As a senior medical man I used to see many patients who had already been investigated in hospital several times by a number of consultants. They had had blood tests without number, X-rays of the kidneys, stomach and bowels, sugar tolerance tests, electro-cardiograms—the lot. Many of them had had several operations. They were difficult problems. I do not profess to have solved them all, indeed some were certainly insoluble.

Some patients were doctors' wives, some were nurses. The *folie à deux* was commonly a factor in their causation: the situation in which husband and wife react upon each other each making the other worse. Abdominal symptoms of a somewhat bizarre nature arise, not conforming to any recognizable pattern of organic disease, but probably connected with an incompatible marriage situation which is not admitted on either side unless blunt questions are asked under confidential conditions. But the symptoms which are probably defensive or attention-seeking or which conceal unhappiness and inadequacy, work upon the other partner, as they are meant to do, who feels guilty and contrite, knowing that the situation may be of his or her making. Much of this is at the unconscious level or is certainly not clearly understood—'you'd better see So-and-so; you'd better see a specialist; you'd better go to hospital; you ought to have an X-ray'—each partner hoping that something will be found which will put right what is really an unsatisfactory interpersonal life situation.

Unfortunately the consultant, having been conditioned by his training always to look for organic causes of symptoms, orders a series of investigations. Perhaps a gallstone shadow is revealed and a gallstone is removed. After an interval in which the life situation is improved, not by the operation but by a temporary resurgence of mutual sympathy, the symptoms take on a new form. This time adhesions are suspected or a 'grumbling appendix' or a displaced uterus. Further operations take place with similar results. At some stage a psychiatrist is called in. Again there may be temporary improvement but psychiatrists vary greatly in their methods, beliefs and wisdom. Sooner or later the patient loses faith and the interviews are no longer helpful. A return to organic thinking takes place. Another specialist finds a disc displacement or an osteopath manipulates the spine or a naturopath prescribes a diet. Whatever happens at this stage only confirms the state of invalidism which has by now long passed the possibility of cure.

Could it ever have been cured? How far is it right to blame the craze for intensive investigation into organic causes? One cannot tell. One can only say that a little more wisdom and an earlier insight into the psychological and personality problems might surely have prevented some of the unnecessary hospital treatment and surgery. But if the symptoms are protecting the patient from facing up to a life situation which is basically intolerable, one can even question whether their cure could be beneficial. Consciously or unconsciously, some people want to be ill.

I may occasionally have helped such patients to gain insight into their situation, but it is more likely that the next I hear of them they have found a wonderful Swiss (or French or Italian or American) doctor who really understands them and is giving them (very expensive) injections to clear a concealed source of infection in the bowel (or something), or has put them on yet another diet requiring careful supervision in an expensive home where they spend a few weeks at a time able to enjoy their invalidism.

There have always been such patients. The supposed causes and cures of their complaints vary from decade to decade as the fashions change in medicine and society. Human nature remains the same. I have little advice to offer. I would say to younger doctors that anyone who has had three or more abdominal operations is almost certainly suffering from psychological rather than organic disease. Don't investigate further. Take a careful history under conditions of strict privacy. Ask boldly about relations with spouse and parents, about attitudes to sex, above all about happiness. You may be surprised at what you unearth which the whole of radiology, biochemistry and surgery has failed to reveal. Beware especially of nurses with bizarre symptoms. At their best nurses are splendid, sensible and devoted people. At their worst they have the little knowledge which is a dangerous thing and all the expertise necessary to play upon the sympathies of others, to start new symptoms when old ones are outworn and to lay the foundations of a life of complacent and egocentric invalidism.

Positive Health

It is important not to confuse health with strength. I have mentioned earlier that Commandos, who had been trained up to the limits of physical fitness and endurance, who could parachute from thousands of feet, climb twenty-foot walls, and swim across icy rivers, had no more resistance to malaria, dysentery and infective hepatitis, which were our three main scourges in North Africa and Italy, than someone like myself who had no athletic prowess and no pretence to physical or muscular strength. I have been heard to say that a good brisk game of chess and a rub down afterwards is my idea of athletic sport, although in my later years I have taken up postcard chess which I find less exhausting though it requires a certain amount of staying power; my last game took nine months.

Nevertheless, physical fitness and a certain amount of athletic sport probably have some effect in delaying the kind of illness which is commoner in the obese and in those who pursue sedentary occupations. There is some evidence, though not very secure, that coronary heart disease is commoner in those who do not take physical exercise and that obesity is to some extent co-related with diabetes, with hypertension (high blood pressure) and with heart failure. But this may only mean that the kind of man who tries to keep physically fit is less likely to be a cigarette addict and an alcoholic than the kind of man whose life consists largely of business luncheons and board meetings.

It is particularly in this type of individual that the periodic, perhaps annual, 'check-up' may be of some use. The 'boardroom' type of man who is smoking too much, drinking too much, putting on weight, and whose blood pressure is gradually rising may perhaps be deterred before it is too late by a regular interview with a wise doctor whose personality is sufficient to get the message across. The heavy cigarette smoker should, I suppose, be advised to have an X-ray of the lungs periodically, but let him not think that this will protect him from dying of lung cancer because as soon as it shows in an X-ray it is, in the majority of cases, already too late.

Most of the other serious hazards of middle life are only very rarely amenable to early diagnosis. A man of middle-age may have his chest X-rayed and his heart examined and his electro-cardiagram pronounced normal, and die within twenty-four hours from coronary thrombosis. If you submitted yourself to an annual X-ray of the stomach and the bowel, it is possible that in a tiny proportion of cases cancer of the stomach or the bowel might be detected in an early and curable stage, but to have X-ray examinations of this intensity at frequent intervals is itself a hazard, and very early cancer is extremely difficult to detect. If a considerable number of people had this kind of examination as a matter of routine there would, in fact, be a large number of false clues; people would be subjected to more and more X-ray examinations with a view to showing whether the uncertain shadow revealed on the first examination was of any serious import. By the time this had gone on for a few years the patient might have become a hypochondriac whether he was suffering from cancer or not.

In short, I think the kind of advice I have given earlier in this chapter as to the symptoms which really might be indicative of serious disease is probably better preventive medicine than the annual routine investigation.

I cherish a story told to me by a general practitioner friend many years ago which, he said, illustrated a triumph of modern medicine. An old man came into the surgery one evening. 'Hello,' said my friend George, 'how are you?' 'I'm all right,' said the old man, 'except I'm just a bit dizzy in me 'ead.' George examined him very thoroughly to see if he could find any cause for this and in the course of his examination he thought he detected some rather serious abdominal disease in an early stage; it was imperative to have it examined to see if some surgical procedure was necessary before it was too late. He called in a surgical friend who agreed with him and took the old man into hospital where he had a large number of investigations and ended up with an operation which had to be done in two stages. This was before the days of antibiotics and there were complications which prevented the immediate healing of the surgical wounds. Altogether the old chap was in hospital for two or three months, after which he was sent to a convalescent home and eventually returned to his own home. Soon after this he again visited my friend in his surgery. George said to him 'Hello, it's a long time since I've seen you. How are you getting on?' 'I'm all right, doctor,' he said, 'but I'm just a bit dizzy in me 'ead.'

7. *Ethical Problems of Human Experiment*

Experiments by doctors on their patients are not new; there has always been a first time in the use of a new drug, or a new means of prevention, or the performance of a new operation. The open-air treatment of pulmonary tuberculosis was in its time thought to be as potentially dangerous an innovation as some new drugs and operations are today.

Two of the most courageous, deliberately planned experiments of former centuries were attempts to immunize against smallpox and as landmarks in medical progress deserve description. Smallpox in the unprotected is a terrible disease and was rife in England in the seventeenth and eighteenth centuries. It was often fatal, sometimes caused blindness, and if the patient survived it would leave the face and body scarred badly for life.

The inoculation of material from a smallpox pustule into a scratch on the arm had long been used in some Eastern countries, and in 1717 Lady Mary Wortley Montagu, returning from Turkey where her husband had been ambassador, introduced it into England. When successful it produced a mild form of the disease which was said to cause lasting immunity. It was first tried out on six condemned criminals and the popularity of the method was later enhanced by several royal persons who submitted themselves to the procedure.

Thomas Dimsdale, a practitioner in Hertford won a high reputation for his skill in this method of inoculation and was requested by the Empress Catherine of Russia to come to St Petersburg and inoculate herself and her son. After making suitable arrangements for his escape from Russia, should any disastrous result occur, he accepted the invitation and the inoculations were a complete success. Besides the royal personages he treated many others in St Petersburg and in Moscow, earning great fame and reward.

Later in the century, Edward Jenner, a practitioner in a village in Gloucestershire heard it said that dairy-maids who had contracted cowpox (which, when conveyed to the human subject causes only a mild eruption on the hands of the milker) considered that they were immune from smallpox. A mild and normally rather timid man, Jenner contemplated for some twenty years the idea of deliberately inoculating cowpox, and in 1796 he tried the experiment and vaccinated (a new word then) a boy of eight from the hand of an infected dairy-maid. Eight weeks later he put his experiment to the crucial test by inoculating the boy with smallpox and finding that it produced no disease. As is well known, vaccination was later made compulsory, and smallpox has virtually disappeared from every country where this has become normal practice. Jenner is thus hailed as one of the pioneers of modern preventive medicine and one of the greatest benefactors of mankind. He was richly rewarded by the State, but preferred to continue his country practice rather than make his fortune in London.

I have called these experiments courageous, as undoubtedly they were. But what should we have called them if the Empress and the boy had both died? Would the ethics of medical practice and experiment today have permitted them? Undoubtedly not. Experiments on criminals are not allowed in this country, and as to inoculating material from a deadly disease into a boy of eight, even if the tremendous importance of the experiment seemed to justify it, a child cannot give consent, neither can a parent give consent to any procedure which might harm the child. Actually, it must be said that Jenner's experiment could have been carried out on an adult volunteer, but of course by adult years many persons must have developed a natural immunity, doctors especially, so the experiment would not have been such a good one, scientifically speaking.

I do not know what moral is to be drawn or what lesson is to be learnt from this, except that the making of laws and rules which have to do with human life and death is an impossible task. It is therefore all the more necessary that anyone who is concerned with human experiment must be always conscious of the responsibility that he holds.

In recent years, for a variety of reasons, the problems have become more acute. Drugs and operations are much more powerful, for good or ill, than they used to be, and when safety measures such as modern anaesthesia and cardiac monitoring during operations keep up with the potential hazards, an operation which would have been inevitably fatal some years ago now becomes a relatively minor risk. Paradoxically this can make the decisions even more difficult. An example is in the treatment of certain congenital defects of the heart. As long as the operation is 'new' and hazardous, conscience dictates that it shall be used only for the desperately ill patient whose expectation of life is otherwise no more than a few months. Put the situation bluntly to him and he will usually opt for the operation. The surgeon is content if his mortality is no more than twenty-five per cent, so long as the successes are worthwhile and life-saving. But with practice and improved technique born of experience it is surprising how soon, in some instances, the dangerous operation becomes relatively safe. The mortality is now, shall we say five per cent. Do we advise patients who have this defect but are at present quite well, to have the operation while they are still 'good operative risks' in order to prevent cardiac breakdown later in life? Do we risk a fatal outcome in a person of twenty-five (even though the risk is now small) because he is unlikely to live to be more than forty without it?

There is of course no easy or universal way out of these dilemmas. Judgment based on experience and with a strong sense of ethical responsibility is all that we can call upon. Even statistics do not help very much, for the target is a rapidly moving one, and results published even a year or two ago are already out of date.

Clearly I cannot go into each ethical problem of modern medicine and surgery in such detail.

Let us return to why there are new problems. Firstly, as I have said, because of the rapid progress of medical science, secondly because of the organization of clinical science and experiment and thirdly because of the almost equally rapid social and educational change in our patients.

In my days as a young hospital doctor, every man was, in a sense, for himself. Every surgeon and physician had his own one or two junior assistants, and was dependent on private practice for a living. Every surgeon was therefore the rival (however friendly) of his colleagues. This did not make for team-work and the organization of research. Research work was unpaid and however devoted some physicians and surgeons were to the exploration of new ideas, private practice had to come first and soon overwhelmed the spare hours that might have been used for research. With the development, largely after the Second World War, of university departments in which both the aim and the reward was teaching and research, this was all changed. New ideas, often originating from the laboratory, from sister sciences (such as physics and chemistry) or from the pharmaceutical industry, could be tried out or explored by deliberately planned trials.

And the patients? As a whole they are incomparably better informed (if only by the accident of switching on the wrong radio or television programme) and much better provided for than the hospital patients of my day. When seriously ill they were, in those days, the objects of charity; grateful, usually, but uncomprehending. One did one's best, but if the drug did not work or produced ill effects, or the operation proved fatal there were few who would raise ethical considerations and stand in judgment.

Let us take first the trial of a new drug. It has been developed by one of the pharmaceutical firms; its action and potential dangers have been thoroughly tested on animals and on some human volunteers. It is meant to control blood pressure perhaps, or to be a useful sedative or to cause diuresis (increased urinary flow). Altogether it is not a very alarming situation, and most doctors would not think it necessary to explain to a patient that he was performing an experiment in order to try it out. The trial should be properly organized, some patients having the new remedy and some the old so that their effects can be compared, a controlled trial in fact is planned.

But no amount of testing can make every drug absolutely safe, if only because humans may react differently from animals and because the hazards may be rare and due to some personal, presumably biochemical, idiosyncrasy of the patient. For instance there is an antibiotic valuable in typhoid fever which once in thousands of cases causes severe destruction of bone marrow tissue leading to an anaemia which may be fatal. Obviously its use is justified in a serious disease like typhoid fever, but not in a minor self-limiting disease such as tonsillitis. Then there was the unforeseen tragedy of the effect of thalidomide on the unborn child. Recent legislation is doing its best to prevent these tragedies but where powerful remedies are in use there can never be a hundred per cent safety.

Sometimes the benefit of a new drug may be marginal and very careful experimental design may be necessary to make sure that the apparently good results are not merely the result of suggestion. The double-blind trial may then be used. The patients are chosen at random, some receiving the new drug, some the old, or some a 'placebo', for instance a tablet which looks the same as the real tablet but consists of some harmless substance having no demonstrable pharmacological action. Neither the patient nor the doctor in charge knows who is on the drug and who is not, so that neither the enthusiasm of the doctor nor the excitement of the patient in taking a new remedy can bias the result. Only when the results in all patients have been studied and compared is it revealed, by the person holding the random selection cards, which patients have had the drug.

This raises a number of ethical problems, for instance whether one should ever deceive a patient (unless it is deemed to be for his benefit, like withholding information which might provoke anxiety) and whether the subjects of an experiment should be chosen at random. Certain it is, that such a trial should never be done unless the doctor is genuinely uncertain whether the new remedy is better than existing treatment, and in my opinion controlled trials with placebos should never be used without the patient's collaboration; that is, all the patients involved should know they are part of an experiment. As a rule, when asked, they will readily acquiesce. But even this does not free the doctor from his ethical responsibility, for he cannot expect the patient to understand all the implications or possible dangers of giving or withholding treatment. It is not enough to say 'I would do this myself' for one must not attribute to the patient the same enthusiasm for medical experiment which is natural to a medical scientist.

An experiment is not necessarily one in therapy, that is, the treatment of the patient. It may be a new and potentially dangerous method of investigation, but similar considerations apply so long as the aim is the good of the patient.

One is on much less safe ground when one is doing an experiment *not* for the investigation or treatment of the individual, but to gain new knowledge of disease (for instance the reaction of the diseased heart or kidney under conditions of stress) which may some day, by generally contributing to knowledge, pave the way to better treatment for some future patient.

There is no doubt that some of these investigations must be made if medical progress is to continue. There is also no doubt that the ethical problems raised should be discussed before any such experiment is contemplated, and that the patient after explanation should be a willing collaborator. Fortunately most of these experiments are virtually harmless and cause no more than some temporary discomfort or inconvenience, but there is no doubt that a few investigators in their enthusiasm for discovery have sometimes gone too far and have subjected patients to unnecessary and unwarranted risks. Such people risk not only their patients but the confidence of the public in medical science and practice.

Other ethical problems arise in the case of preventive medicine; the use of poliomyelitis vaccine, for instance, on a large scale at a time when, however carefully tested, its possible dangers cannot be completely ruled out. Here we are asking the individual to submit for the benefit of society rather than of himself.

The potential dangers of the contraceptive pill present another problem and emphasize once again the impossibility of making absolute decisions where we are concerned with biological matters. Here we are not treating a disease, but trying to prevent an unwanted pregnancy by the most *reliable* and *convenient* method known. But it is not the only method of contraception and though the risk is minute, the occasional deaths which have unquestionably been caused by the pill must all be considered avoidable and usually particularly tragic as they have occurred in apparently healthy women, often with young families.

Organ transplantation has again raised new ethical problems, for here we have the donor to consider as well as the recipient. Assuming that an organ from a dead subject is to be used, it must be procured as soon as possible after death. Now that people whose brains are irreversibly damaged by disease or accident can be kept 'alive' by artificial respiration, cardiac pacemaking and intravenous feeding, their moment of 'death' can be conveniently arranged by switching off the apparatus. Laws and codes may establish the circumstances under which such a procedure should be permitted. Science may improve further on the present tests of cerebral viability, but no law can apply to every case, unless it is to prohibit organ transplantation completely. Even so it would have to be carefully framed if corneal grafting and blood transfusion are still to continue, for both are forms of organ transplantation.

In my opinion, and contrary to the views of some others, the publicity given to organ (especially cardiac) transplantation is not wholly regrettable for two reasons. First, I think publicity of this kind is rapidly influencing public opinion (and may eventually influence legal opinion) on matters of life, death and human experiment. Secondly, I think it is more difficult for bad, bold, reckless surgeons (if there be any!) to get away with an unjustifiable experimental procedure in a blaze of publicity

75

than if it was behind the closed doors of an old-fashioned poor-law hospital.

Ethics is finally a matter for the public conscience, and ethical codes will change from time to time with public opinion. It is difficult to ask relatives at a time of great distress whether you can rip out the heart and kidneys of a dying wife, son or mother. In my view we shall, perhaps quite soon, reach a position in which such an action becomes permissible (provided precautions laid down as to criteria of brain-death are satisfied), in all cases unless the individual, in his lifetime, or his near relatives specifically object. But I doubt if the time has yet come for the promotion of a bill of this kind.

8. *Ageing and Death*

In 1956 I gave an address on 'Life'* to the Manchester Medical Society which ended with these words:

> ... a wise man, at any rate when he reaches the post-reproductive age, should meditate now and then upon death, if only to face it courageously should it announce its coming in advance. Though perhaps not with the morbid preoccupation of Charles Morgan's *Sparkenbroke*, I nevertheless find death a fascinating subject; and perhaps at some future time I may be permitted to address you on that theme. If so, I shall, of course, be under the handicap of not being able to speak from personal experience.

An important fact, well known to students of the subject of ageing, is that there seems to be a human lifespan whose mode, or maximum effect, is at about seventy-six years, around which are the peak years of death from the natural processes of ageing, as opposed to death due to the environmental hazards of life, such as accident and infection. Above the age of seventy-six deaths get fewer because the population is less. Medical science, and engineering, chemical and other sciences which have contributed so much to the conquest of bacterial disease and malaria, have reduced the deaths due to environment, so that far more people than formerly live into old age. Thus the *average* age at death has been notably postponed, simply because more people live to be old. But the lifespan, which is determined by arterial and general deterioration and by cancer in old age, has hardly changed. The expectation of life for a man or woman of about seventy-seven is still only a few years.

* See *The Lancet* 14.1.56, p. 61.

There are however certain other interesting things about the lifespan. At all ages women have a better expectation of life than men, so much so that at sixty a man has almost twice the likelihood of dying before sixty-one than a woman has. This is why grandmothers are much commoner than grandfathers, and why, I am told, more than half the capital of the United States is in the hands of widows.

This great difference between men and women has increased very appreciably in recent years. It may be that in a modern society grandmothers are more important than grandfathers for the survival of the race, and so natural selection has been at work again. It may be cigarettes, but this can be considered later. In any case it does not account for the whole of the difference of lifespan between the sexes; a long survival of females is known in some of the non-smoking animal species.

Mortality in middle years is also influenced by genetic factors. Some studies of my own have shown the great importance of heredity in high blood pressure, for instance. Brothers and sisters of patients attending for the treatment of hypertension have eight times the likelihood of high blood pressure than is to be found in the general population. By a carefully designed system of breeding (which is most unlikely to be adopted), high blood pressure as a common and important cause of death in middle age could be eliminated in a few generations.

What chance is there of postponing the process of senescence and thus lengthening the lifespan? Here there are also some pointers, but they do not point in the direction of anything very practical. Experiments have been made by various investigators in which young growing animals are kept in a state of undernutrition. This leads to delay in maturity, a considerable mortality early in life and (in some cases, but not all) a significant lengthening of the lifespan of the survivors. Conversely, the earlier sexual maturity of the present generation of humans in Britain and their quicker arrival at full physical stature, is usually attributed to better nutrition. But it has been pointed out that this has taken place since the invention of the bicycle and may be due to what is known as hybrid vigour or heterosis; in other words, outbreeding has very largely replaced the former inbreeding of the isolated village community.

There are numerous examples in biology of interbreeding causing increased resistence to disease and environmental hazards, with consequent longevity. It remains to be seen whether the modal lifespan of our present early-maturing children will be longer or shorter than that of their ancestors. We could also breed directly for longevity if we wished, because there is ample evidence, since Galton, that inheritance is involved; some families regularly produce nonagenarians and even centenarians.

Summing up what I have said so far, we see that the chances of dying are divided into two groups, the hazards and deterioration; the hazards have already been greatly diminished in intensity. The chances of dying at ten or twenty are less than thirty per cent of what they were fifty years ago. This is a notable change to anyone who, like me, has been in medicine for over forty years. Indeed, you do not need to be in medicine. You have only to read biographies of the eighteenth and nineteenth century—the Brontës and Darwins and Mrs Thrale, for instance—to know how the dread effects of infectious illness were ever present in the minds of parents. In my time we did not see smallpox and plague in this country, but pneumonia, septicaemia, scarlet fever and tuberculosis were common enough as killing diseases in young persons.

Later in life the process of deterioration seems to be inevitable, and the likelihood of being able to alter the lifespan significantly at present seems to be remote. It seems probable from recent work that the ageing process is linked with abnormalities in the chromosomes, as if the constant replacement of cells which goes on throughout our lives leads gradually to more and more inaccuracy in the copying process of cell reproduction. As we know that chromosome abnormalities are also common in leukaemia and in cancer cells, it is an easy step to link up the increasing liability to malignant disease with age to inaccuracies in cell division. Thus cancer may perhaps occupy a special position in the mortality of ageing persons, bridging

79

the gap between the effects of environment and those of deterioration.

A falling-off in fertility, potency, and sexual desire is something on which comment has been made since Biblical times and before, and is referred to with surprising complacency in Cicero's *De senectute*. Osbert Sitwell, speaking of one of his father's friends, says, 'He was so old that the spring could do nothing for him but to make him more tired.' Many have been the therapeutic measures recommended by doctors, sages and poets. Although fertility in women ceases fairly suddenly at about the time of the menopause, anxious persons approaching middle age are often reassured to learn that sex life does not terminate abruptly in either sex but often continues into the seventh or even the eighth decade. I remember an old lady telling me that she was surprised at what could happen after sixty and even seventy. Sir Harold Nicolson has noted with some sadness that desire and desirability do not decline together. Ageing males sometimes develop an increasing interest in the company of young females. If this remains within the realm of innocent fantasy, like Johnson's wish to drive in a post-chaise with a pretty woman, it can be an acceptable mode of gracious living; but it sometimes leads to inappropriate marriages between very old and very young, or in its more aggravated and senile form to the old man being allowed out only with a keeper.

Turning now from sexual behaviour to biological fact, there is no firm evidence to suggest that transplants of ovarian or testicular tissue can rejuvenate; but that is not to deny that sexual function can be influenced by sex hormones.

The storage of spermatozoa and ova at low temperatures, with preservation of their function, has been achieved in animals, and the storage by hypothermia of organs (and, indeed, of whole individuals), thus temporarily defeating the effects of ageing, is already in the stage of animal experiment. Biostasis, as A. S. Parkes observes, holds nothing new in principle, being woven into the fabric of countless human beliefs, legends and stories, from the resurrection of the dead to the awakening of Sleeping Beauty.

To a large extent popular beliefs about the change of mental function with age are based on sound observation. Variability in mental performance in old age is one of the most notable features and occurs similarly in rats and other animals. Some experiments have shown that about forty per cent of a sample number of old rats are not able to learn maze problems which are new to them, whereas sixty per cent learn them only a little more slowly than younger rats. Similarly when a maze has been learnt earlier in life about forty per cent will remember it well. In humans original discoveries and great works are usually achieved before the age of forty, but there have been some very notable exceptions, especially in art, literature, and music. Richard Strauss's very beautiful Four Last Songs, for instance, were composed when he was eighty-four.

In science I think the lack of achievement in middle age may be due to the tendency of university research workers to go on working at essentially the same problem all their lives and to use essentially the same approach to it. The law of diminishing returns will then ensure that nothing very new is likely to emerge. Some say that the limit of interest in a job is ten to twelve years and from my own experience (which sociologists might call a bad employment record) I would incline to agree and to advise men in established intellectual careers to change their interests from time to time.

Experiments show that older people tend to score well on tests requiring verbal comprehension, but less well on facing fresh situations and learning new information. On the whole there is a slowing down of sensorimotor activities where some signal must be perceived and lead to action; but again there are large differences between individuals, some even in their seventies performing as well as the average for the age of twenty. Some of the slowing may be due to the caution born of experience. In general most old persons still in employment are to be found in moderately heavy jobs. 'Light work', often demanding speed and fine visual judgment, as for instance in the conveyor-belt type of factory, is usually unsuitable.

The next most widely observed mental change in age is loss of short-term memory, and this itself may impair the programming of action. An example of failing short-term memory came my way a year or two ago. At dinner at the Athenaeum I sat next to one of the older members.

'What's that you're drinking?' said he.

'The *vin ordinaire*,' I replied.

'As I get older I find I can only drink gin and champagne' and then, 'Is that a Bishop over there by the window?'

'Yes, it is.'

'Which Bishop is it, I wonder. Do you know?'

'I'm not very good at Bishops but I think it's Barchester.'

'He's not wearing gaiters. I think if they are Bishops they ought to wear gaiters.'

'Well, perhaps they find it too hot in the evenings.'

'I still think they ought to wear them.'

I then got into conversation with my neighbour on the other side; but, there being later a lull in the conversation, the old man returned to me.

'Is that a Bishop over there by the window?'

'Yes, I think it is.'

'I wonder which Bishop it is. Do you know?'

'I think it is Barchester.'

'He's got a grey suit on.'

'But he has a purple thing under his collar which probably shows he's a Bishop.'

'I still think they should dress like Bishops if they are going to be Bishops. I suppose he signs his name in Latin. I wonder what the Latin for Barchester is....'

Intelligent old people often learn as well as young ones, even if more slowly, and qualities of judgment may be long preserved. There are personality differences of course, and those few who are blessed with rarer qualities of mind and originality of thought may go on maturing, like Sherrington, into great old age. Old people, if they preserve their intellectual powers, can be fascinating companions, and younger men should seek their company more often than they do.

Another dear old club member, for whom we all had a great affection, once said to me 'I'm getting so blind now it's difficult to recognize people and I don't know whether to smile or scowl; so I always scowl to be on the safe side.'

I am not particularly interested in the physical changes of death nor competent to discuss them; nor do I want to enter here into philosophical discussions of what death is, or forensic ones as to when it takes place. Death, as we ordinarily use the term, refers to the end of the corporate life of the clone of cells which constitutes the individual. It does not refer necessarily to each of the cells or tissues considered separately. Recent experiments have demonstrated that skin cells could be grown in culture two months after the estimated death of a foetus *in utero*. The cells must still have been alive.

What I want to speak of is a physician's experience of the way in which men and women meet death. It is an intimate matter, not easy to write about, and yet deserving of more attention than is usually given to it by medical authors. By meeting death I mean the recognition that an illness will probably or inevitably be fatal. In my sense of the term a large number of people do not have to face death at all. If they die suddenly of disease or accident, they may have to face it for an agonized moment of which there is usually no record; but many are robbed of their senses by delirium or coma, or by the brain-damage of disease or senility. Old people adjust more to a state of progressive weakness and limited activity than to the threat of death, and when death comes it may do so quite suddenly. 'The aged,' wrote Sir Thomas Lewis (a pioneer in the investigation of heart disease), 'pass out unobtrusively after brief illness, or without warning, while sitting in their chairs or sleeping in their beds.' But it is not always so, though death often holds

83

little terror for the really old. Many of them, infirm and dependent on others, are quite ready to die and will tell you so.

Sometimes younger persons feel the same after long and wearying illness. Such a one was a Scandinavian patient of mine, a man of great courage who had defied the Germans during the occupation of Denmark. He had progressive pulmonary fibrosis, of what origin we never discovered even at post mortem examination. After some years of increasing discomfort and disablement he was again admitted to hospital and asked one of the nurses what time of the day or night it would be least inconvenient for a patient to die. Having apparently been given this piece of information, he was found dead at that time on the following day. We never knew his secret.

With doctor patients there are some who know only too well, but will carry on as long as possible as if nothing much has happened, even after making their own diagnosis of incurable cancer. Others try to cling to some pathetically inadequate explanation for their symptoms.

Lay people are naturally interested to know a doctor's view on what he should tell his patients; but, in fact, the question does not arise as often as one might think; for a conspiracy of silence usually surrounds the whole question of death, a silence as much due to the patient's avoidence of the subject as the doctor's. Patients do not frequently seek to have their worst fears confirmed, and some I am sure are unwilling to put their doctors into an embarrassing position; for there is abundant evidence that patients are most considerate of their doctors' feelings in these matters. In the days when there was no effective treatment for chronic pulmonary tuberculosis I remember a man who attended the tuberculosis clinic telling me that they always weighed him, and that he used to put stones in his pockets, 'so as not to disappoint the doctors'.

Some patients, while not inviting discussion, find ways of letting you know that they know. Some are quite frank about it. When I visited a patient with acute heart failure late one evening many years ago, after speaking some words which were intended to be reassuring, I said to him 'I'll see you in the morning.' 'Yes I know, doctor', he replied, 'but will I see you?'

If we read history and literature we may gain the impression that it is common for patients on their deathbeds to make long addresses, couched in elegant terms, to their assembled attendants and relatives. It has not been my experience that this is a normal feature of the deathbed scene; neither have I known the dying person leaning on one elbow against some pillows to burst into song, like Mimi, Isolde, or Mélisande. No doubt the deathbed speech was commoner in past centuries than it is today; for a certain weight and pomposity of expression was expected from great men, and the possibility of death from violence or disease must have been ever present in their minds. Cardinal Wolsey and Cromwell both made deathbed speeches, if we are to believe contemporary accounts: the first accurately foretelling his end and the second denying its possibility. Accounts of the death of Charles II vary, but it is at least possible that his famous apology for being such an unconscionable time a-dying was authentic. It tallies well with my experience of patients' consideration for their doctors.

A very famous surgeon on the day that he died thanked me for coming so early in the morning and then said 'I always feel I ought to think up something to say to cheer up my physician, but this morning I must say I find it mighty difficult.' And another medical friend, stricken with serious illness, said to me 'I thought this kind of thing only happened to patients.'

I have no doubt at all that most patients faced with dangerous or mortal illness recognize their danger, if their mind is clear, though perhaps few regard death as inevitable. The occasions may be rare when a discussion on death, at the bedside, is appropriate; but I think more opportunity should be given for such discussions if the patient indicates a wish for them. Far too often he is almost forced into the conspiracy of silence, for if his first approaches are met with an immediate rebuff by the doctor, who brushes aside all likelihood of a fatal outcome, the patient is not encouraged to express his fears or

85

discuss his feelings. He keeps them privately to himself, but the doctor is mistaken if he thinks his superficial reassurances are accepted. He has merely given the patient the impression that the voicing of his most intimate thoughts and fears will be unwelcome. Precisely the same happens when the patient talks to his friends and relatives. To speak of death is distressing, embarrassing, distasteful; the subject is mutually avoided.

For this reason I do not accept unreservedly the statements of many doctors that patients should never be told of impending death, that they do not want to know or to discuss it, and that in their long experiences they have never known a patient express the wish to die. Perhaps they have always rejected the initial overtures that open the way to frank discussion. My own mother certainly expressed to me her wish to die a few days before her death occurred.

You may then ask how I feel so certain that most patients realize the situation, even though they may still cling to the slight hope that there may be some last-minute reprieve. Firstly, because I have always thought it right not to discourage them if they seem to want to talk, though I have usually tried to keep the conversation on hopeful themes such as 'we have to face the possibilities, but I can tell you that I have seen patients just as ill recover eventually' or that 'the X-ray looks as if it must be cancer, but there is always the chance that it may be proved wrong'. My feeling, difficult to say with assurance, is that most people like to be left with just a little gleam of hope.

Secondly, I think it is quite in order to discuss death at the bedside in retrospect when recovery from danger has clearly set in. This can often be done with patients who have had a coronary heart attack. If you ask them how they felt during the acute period of pain and shock, they will nearly all say, as is well known, that they thought their end had come, though even now circumlocution is the rule: rarely is the word death bluntly mentioned.

Thirdly, there are those whom I have mentioned who drop hints to you, clear signals that, though they accept the conventions of secrecy and silence, they are not to be fooled. One of these was a doctor in Manchester, whose memory I have always respected. At the age of only fifty-one he had severe high blood pressure and had already suffered two strokes. I saw him a number of times and I could never quite discern what he really made of his illness. He seemed to treat it as if it were all rather trivial and I wondered if cerebral damage had dulled his powers of judgment. I was not his regular attendant but only an adviser from time to time. One day I said to him, 'I needn't see you regularly, but you must let me know how you go on.' As he left the room he said, 'Look in *The Guardian*.' The sequel is interesting to those who have a taste for psychic research. I never normally looked at the deaths column of *The Guardian*, but a few months later for some reason I did. On that very day his name appeared.

Perhaps this brings us to what happens after death, and perhaps I am not qualified to discuss it. The Christian religion teaches that you should live this life and prepare for death in the belief of a life to come. The same or similar beliefs are common in other religions. Cicero clearly believed in an after-life when he wrote *De senectute*. I can only say that there are some who find such beliefs out of line with Man's present knowledge of his place in the biological world. The glimpses into the thoughts and feelings of men and women on the threshold of death, which as a doctor I have been privileged to witness, leave me in no doubt that there are many who can come to terms with the inevitable and who can derive courage and strength and even comfort by living their lives and in due course preparing for death, content to believe that life is something which happens but once, and that Death is the end of it.

A thoughtful and sensitive article on the dying patient has been published by Professor Cramond of Adelaide (*The British Medical Journal* 15.8.70, p. 389) in which his considered conclusions are similar to my own, namely that most seriously ill patients do consider death as a possible outcome and many welcome the chance to talk about their feelings. It is usually wrong to persuade the relatives not to reveal the truth but to keep up a kind of transparent deception which only serves to disrupt the ties of affection and understanding which could be so helpful at this time. In fact the usual tendency of doctors to conceal the truth is more often a means of shielding the doctor than the patient, and it is disgraceful that in the teaching of nurses and doctors, whether verbally or by written texts, this important subject is practically never mentioned at all. (Another triumph for the academics and the scientists.)

9. Common Misconceptions about the Medical Profession

Medical etiquette

The written and unwritten codes of medical etiquette are often deemed by the public to have been devised solely for the benefit, especially the financial benefit, of doctors, and as a means of defeating the just demands of their patients. It must be conceded that doctors, especially irresponsible ones, anxious to save themselves any kind of thought or trouble are inclined to shield themselves behind the etiquette, but its real purpose is in fact the protection of the patient.

One of the commonest rules of etiquette in this country, to which exception is often taken, is that a patient should not go to a consultant without being referred by another doctor, usually his general practitioner. Occasional exceptions are and can be made but for the most part it is a good rule. At its best it ensures that the consultant gets a letter (or telephone message) explaining the background of the case and the circumstances of the patient, including in many instances confidential or even embarrassing details which the patient may hesitate to tell to a doctor as yet unknown to him. A good letter from the practitioner can be invaluable in defining the patient's problem. Secondly, it ensures that the patient is properly advised by his practitioner (who should know better than the patient's neighbour or mother-in-law or business partner) which specialist is the best one to consult having regard to the particular nature of the case. Thirdly, it should protect the patient from going to an expensive quack; and fourthly it prevents undesirable competition and rivalry between consultants (who should keep to their specialities) and practitioners, who should be expert in advising on these matters and in dealing with the many cases in which further opinion and investigation is not required.

Finally, the patient who goes to a specialist without his doctor's knowledge and consent and the specialist who accepts him, both store up trouble for the future. Supposing the specialist does advise treatment, for instance by tablets or injections which must be continued for weeks, months or years. Obviously the patient's practitioner must be informed and must supervise the treatment. He may not be pleased that the decisions have been made without his knowledge.

The system, excellent in its conception and purpose, breaks down when pseudo-consultants put up plates in Harley Street and accept all who ring the bell. It breaks down more often because foolish general practitioners resent being asked by their patients if they can consult a specialist, and again if the patient *feels* that they will resent it and so hesitates to suggest it. The doctor who has confidence in his own competence should either give reasons why he thinks a consultation unnecessary, or advise a further trial of ordinary remedies first, or should acquiesce, either because he agrees that a further consultation or investigation might be helpful or because he sees that the patient wishes it and will therefore be more satisfied if he gets it. There should be no loss of face. Resentment at imagined insult and loss of dignity is one of the common faults of bad doctors, based on an inferiority complex, and at worst can lead to an obstinate refusal on the part of the doctor to carry out treatment which is urgently necessary. Finally it should be remembered that in the Health Service every patient has a right to change his doctor and should do so if he thinks the doctor is unnecessarily and perhaps dangerously resisting the idea of a second opinion. I have myself often been saved from making an error, whether serious or trivial, by listening to a patient's own observations and suggestions and taking them seriously. I used to teach my students 'the patient is nearly always right. Take heed of what he says.'

Harley Street

I wish the public would remember that Harley Street is an address and not a qualification. The facts are simply these. For convenience in the first place, and gradually by reputation and prestige, Harley Street and the streets around, such as Wimpole Street and Devonshire Place, have become an area where a large number of the most eminent specialists have their consulting rooms. Because rents and reputations are high, fees are proportionally high and it is therefore to some extent an indication of success that you are able to practise there and that patients come to consult you. But there is no entrance fee, there is no examination to pass, there is no body of learned men to say whether you may or may not practise in this specific location.

There is in fact no law of this land to say that you must have a medical qualification at all to practise anywhere. The law merely says that you must not pretend to a medical qualification that you do not possess, and that without a medical qualification you cannot prescribe certain drugs nor sign a death certificate.

Anyone may rent a room in Harley Street and, because it is a centre where eminent men practise, it is also attractive to all kinds of cranks and quacks without any higher qualification who call themselves 'Harley Street Specialists' but have no claim to distinction beyond an aptitude to prescribe unnecessary and expensive treatment to credulous clients.

How then to distinguish the genuine from the fake, the crank, the quack and the impostor?

First ask the advice of your own practitioner; secondly find out not merely the qualifications (a lot of letters do not necessarily make good doctors) of the man you are to see, but what hospital staff he is on (or was on if he has retired from hospital practice). Nearly all reputable specialists have hospital appointments. An appointment to Guy's Hospital means you are someone who has been highly trained and selected; an address in Harley Street by itself means nothing at all and, if not backed by a reputable hospital appointment, immediately arouses suspicion amongst those who know the profession.

Are there not a few really clever men who are not orthodox in their treatment and yet can do much good for their patients?

The answer is 'Yes', but they are few and far between and usually effect their cures by playing upon the credulity of their patients. Even this, if not too costly, may be worthwhile and may provide a little welcome relief to the harassed doctor who has too long struggled with the fads and fancies which are the basis of Mrs Blake-Montmorency's colitis. If she has found a *wonderful* Harley Street man (preferably with a foreign name and accent) who has miraculously discovered just *exactly* the injection she needs, which *has* to be sent from America twice a week, my advice is let her enjoy it (and let her doctor lie back and enjoy it too).

The General Medical Council

Perhaps one day the public will cease to confuse the B.M.A. with the G.M.C. The General Medical Council (G.M.C.) is a statutory body which was set up as a novel experiment in 1858, and has forty-seven members, some nominated by the Queen on the advice of the Privy Council, some elected by the profession, others representing universities and colleges which give degrees and diplomas in Medicine. It has a duty to keep the Medical Register, instituted by the medical act of 1858. It lays down minimal requirements for degrees and diplomas in Medicine and from time to time supervises university and college examinations. At one time criticized for conservatism, its educational policy in recent years has been helpful, enlightened and in keeping with the requirements of the modern doctor.

It also has important disciplinary functions: investigating charges of professional misconduct brought to its notice, such as improper use and prescription of dangerous drugs, abuse of alcohol, adultery with a patient, culpable neglect of professional duty, advertising, issuing untrue or misleading certificates, and so forth. It has the power of erasing a doctor's name from the Medical Register, which is a very severe penalty for him, as well as for his wife and his children for it means that he can no longer practise medicine as a registered practitioner and loses any appointment he may hold under the Health Service. His name may be reinstated after one or more years, on evidence of good conduct during the intervening period.

It is of course important that doctors should be professionally beyond reproach; that they should practise ethically and not abuse their privileges, and that women should be able to call them in or visit them without fear of their taking advantage of the intimacy of the medical consultation. There is no room for rogues, for drunken scoundrels, for advertising sharks and promiscuous rascals in the profession. Yet erasure with consequent loss of all professional earning seems in some instances to be too harsh a penalty for a man generally thought to be a decent chap, respected for his skill and as a person, who, being the recipient of a woman's intimate confessions of unhappiness in her married state, develops a fondness for her which she reciprocates and does nothing to discourage. In time it overwhelms them. Such situations occur in ordinary life so frequently that in modern society we accept them however regrettable the consequences may be to marriage and children. At least we do not seek to add bankruptcy to an already distressing situation. So long as even the threat of possible erasure remains it seems unlikely that some relaxation would lead to a more promiscuous profession, and it does appear that the G.M.C. has recently taken a less rigid view of this kind of case.

The B.M.A.

The British Medical Association, on the other hand, is what it calls itself, a purely medical association which all reputable medical men and women may join on presenting a formal application and paying the appropriate fee. Most of them do join, because they then receive the very informative and practical journal at reduced price, they may make use of the well-stocked library, may attend local B.M.A. lectures and social functions, play their part in medical politics if they wish, and benefit by the undoubted fact that one of the functions of the B.M.A. is to look after their financial interests.

It has always been regarded as the body which looks after the general practitioner rather than the consultant, whose loyalty is more to the Royal Colleges. Since most doctors are members of the B.M.A. it has by common consent become the chief negotiating body with the Government on Health Service matters, though there is a joint committee of the B.M.A. and the Colleges which negotiates for the hospital doctors.

There is no need to join the B.M.A. It has no disciplinary powers and no statutory position or special prestige. I resigned from the British Medical Association in 1948 during the dispute at the time of the inauguration of the Health Service, for it seemed to me that the B.M.A., having accepted the principle of a free health service for all, were now, when faced with reality, trying to do everything possible to prevent its coming about. I pointed out in a somewhat wicked letter to *The Lancet* headed 'Gerontocracy in our time' that they were largely governed by 'old men'. I quoted verbatim from their own report of a meeting, but inserted the ages of all the doctors mentioned:
'... Dr J. B. Miller (72) of Bishopbriggs, presided. He was supported by Dr H. Guy Dain (77), the Chairman of Council, Sir Hugh Lett, Bt. (72), President, Dr J. W. Bone (79) Treasurer, and other Officers of the Association.

'After two congratulatory motions had been passed Lord Horder (77) referred to a cabinet minister who had spoken of the negotiating committee as a "handful of elderly doctors dictating to the profession". In the public interest it seemed desirable to nail these lies to the counter. (Applause) ...'

The British Medical Association is not technically a trade union but it carries out many of the functions of the unions and tends to be bedevilled by two of their besetting sins, namely democracy, and democracy's inevitable companion the *agent provocateur*. Any organization whose strength rests in its

voting power is bound to create, or at least to build up, griev-
ances in order to achieve that treacherous and doubtful benefit,
'solidarity'. You cannot get eighty or ninety per cent of the
medical profession to threaten withdrawal from the Health
Service without building up a mighty grievance, and in doing so
you are in danger of winning a pyrrhic victory; gaining perhaps
a minor concession at the cost of the morale of the profession.

That was my analysis of the situation in 1948 and it has
happened a number of times. Doctors instead of being told of
the advantages of a Health Service were told that it would lead
to second-rate medicine and all kinds of disasters. But the
initiation of a Health Service had already been agreed by all
parties in Parliament and by the B.M.A. itself. It was the profession's business to make it as good as possible, not to start it
grudgingly in an atmosphere of hatred and mistrust. This was
forcefully said by Lord Moran, then President of the Royal
College of Physicians (by comparison an undemocratic body
which prefers to negotiate by the strength of its leadership
rather than by inflammatory speeches followed by a show of
hands or a count of cards) and he was much criticized for doing
so.

The B.M.A. however is much less conservative and back-
ward-looking than it was in those days, and has many good
works and skilful negotiations to its credit. It is right that the
profession should have a body prepared to examine and criti-
cize any new measure which may be forced upon it by the
government of the day. Its report to the Royal Commission on
Medical Education was in my opinion one of the best that we
received (incidentally one sent in by a body representing clinical
professors was one of the worst). I seem to be on good terms
with its leaders at the present time, and have never hesitated
to consult them on questions of interest to the profession which
come before the House of Lords, such as the Misuse of Drugs
Bill, the Industrial Relations Bill, the reorganization of the
Health Service and such matters, and I have always received
valuable advice.

I have never rejoined, partly because minor outbreaks of the old strike mentality are still liable to creep out from time to time, and partly because as a cross-bench peer speaking for Medicine, as I often do, I think I am in a stronger position if I express myself in my own way, independent of party or of anything suggestive of a pressure group. For the same reason, although I was sympathetic to the Abortion Bill and to the concept of voluntary euthanasia, I did not join the Abortion Law Reform Association or the Euthanasia Society.

The British Medical Association today would, I feel sure, agree that, despite its acknowledged defects, the achievements of the National Health Service have been very great. We are too prone to take it for granted as a recent paper in *The Lancet* (25 July 1970), describing the experience of an English medical professor in the United States, shows.

During this visit my personal experience of the health services was, fortunately, limited, but it nevertheless serves to demonstrate the two most serious weaknesses in the American system —the high cost of inpatient care and the inadequacy of care at the primary level.

Both my wife and I were ill for short periods of time. My illness was relatively minor, but hers was a little more serious and necessitated a 24-hour stay in hospital. The bill for this was about £100, of which a third was for 'hotel charges' (food and accommodation) and the remainder was for the various items of service rendered (drugs, treatment) but excluding physicians' and surgeons' fees. At the beginning of the recent influenza epidemic in December, I also stayed with a friend in Washington (a senior physician in one of the Government medical departments). Both he and his wife suffered severe attacks of influenza during my visit, but received no medical attention. It was apparently out of the question for any doctor to visit patients in their own homes, even in this comparatively affluent area. I returned to Britain the following week, and, as is scarcely surprising, immediately became ill. I called in a general practitioner, who came at once and

visited me every day until I had recovered. The contrast between my own experience and that of my American friends
was, I felt, fairly dramatic.

10. The Royal College of Physicians of London *

The first Parliamentary enactment about medical affairs was the result of a petition presented to King Henry VIII in 1511, the third year of his reign. We do not know who the petitioners were, but the act laid down that no person within the City of London or within seven miles of it should practise as a physician or surgeon unless he was first examined by the Bishop of London or the Dean of St Paul's 'calling to him or them four doctors of physic and for surgery other expert persons in that faculty'. The object was of course to suppress the practice of medicine by unqualified, ignorant and unlearned persons such as 'common artificers, smiths, weavers and women ... to the high Displeasure of God, great Infamy to the Faculty and the grievous Hurt, Damage and Destruction of the King's liege People, most especially of them that cannot discern the cunning from the uncunning'.

A petition by six physicians and Wolsey resulted in the granting, in 1518, of a charter by Henry to establish a college of physicians. The prime mover in this was Thomas Linacre, who became the first president of the college, and remained so until he died in 1524, six years later. The success of the petition may have owed something to the fact that both Wolsey and Henry VIII himself were Linacre's patients. Linacre was not only the true creator of the college, but also at that time its main benefactor, for he gave his library to the college, and for nearly a

---

* Anyone who attempts to write even the briefest sketch of some of the history of the Royal College of Physicians must acknowledge his debt to Sir George Clark who was persuaded by Lord Moran to write the college history. His first two volumes take us up to the Medical Act of 1858, a third volume in collaboration with Dr A. M. Cooke is nearing completion.

hundred years its meetings were held in his house, The Stone House, in Knightrider Street near to St Paul's.

There is no doubt that the organization of physicians as a profession dates from the college's foundation. It was established to ensure the highest professional skills and ethical standards, since, in the words of the charter, it was 'before all things necessary to withstand the attempts of those wicked men who profess medicine more for the sake of their avarice than for the assurance of any good conscience whereby many inconveniences may ensue to the rude and credulous populace'. In more modern terms and in a different society (though still sometimes rude and credulous) it could be said that this is what the college stands for today, and in carrying out these aims it has remained throughout the centuries independent of Church, State or even of the universities, for although they teach the principles of medicine they have no continuing interest in its practice.

Linacre's college was not to be a teaching college, though it had some educational functions, but a body of learned men who met to discuss standards of practice and to examine all who aspired to practise in and around the City of London. Indeed they could no longer practise without the college's licence. There were four censors, as there still are, who acted as examiners but also had disciplinary powers to fine or even imprison anyone who practised illegally. They had the power also to search the apothecaries' shops, to see if their medicines were of the required standard, and that the apothecaries were not engaging in the practice of medicine, for they were not allowed to charge for their advice, but only for the medicines which they sold.

Sir George Clark in his history of the college reminds us that Linacre was brought up in medieval times; his Fellowship of All Souls, which is the first step known to us in his career, dates from the time of Richard III and he was still a boy when Caxton set up his printing press at Westminster Abbey. The new study of Greek and of the Latin Classics had started in Europe, and Linacre spent ten years or more in Italy, at Florence and later at Padua, and was virtually the first to bring this new learning to England. He was thus one of the founders of the Humanist movement in England with which the names of Colet and Erasmus, and later Sir Thomas More, were associated. More learnt Greek from Linacre.

To us today, the translation of the works of Galen from Greek into Latin, on which Linacre was engaged for long periods, seems a somewhat academic exercise, but all medical graduates could read and speak Latin, and the aim was a return to the Greek outlook of discovery and enquiry and a break from scholasticism. It was the beginning of a movement which later blossomed with Harvey, Bacon and Newton, and the Royal Society.

In Linacre's time it was quite usual for a physician to take holy orders, and this he did. In those days of pluralism and patronage, however, it must be admitted that he held a number of offices in different parts of the country at the same time, and it is doubtful if he ever attended to them. At various times he was Rector of Merstham and of Aldington in Kent, Prebend of Easton-in-Gordano, Canon and Prebend at St Stephen's, Westminster, and of South Newbold in York, Rector of Holsworthy in Devon and of Wigan in Lancashire.

Another famous president of the college was John Caius, president for three separate periods from 1555, amounting in all to eleven years. In his time he was physician to Edward VI, Mary and Elizabeth, but fell from favour towards the end of his life because of his adherence to Catholic ritual. He first studied Divinity at Cambridge but went to Padua to study anatomy with the famous Vesalius. He was a man of great energy, a profound classical scholar who started the annals of the college, written meticulously in Latin in his own hand. He also started regular anatomical demonstrations at the college. Attentive to the social and ceremonial side of its activities, he held dinners for the fellows and presented the college with the silver staff or caduceus—a thing of great beauty and perfect balance—which is still carried by the president on ceremonial occasions. His chief contribution to medicine was his discourse on the sweating sickness.

Later in the century, in 1581, the first of the college lectures was founded by Richard Caldwell, president, and Lord Lumley. They continue to the present time and are called the Lumleian Lectures. Originally they were to be anatomical, that being the main foundation of medical knowledge at the time. The lecturer was appointed for a number of years and was expected to cover the whole of human anatomy in lectures spread over six years. For these lectures a special theatre was built, but despite this Linacre's house eventually became inadequate for its purpose and, in 1614, the college moved to a house in Paternoster Row near to St Paul's. Thomas Moundeford was president at the time, of whom we know little except that he was 'as good a scholar as any in his time', and that at a dinner held to inaugurate the new college building he made a speech in which he praised the King and denounced smoking.

It was in this building, the second home of the college that William Harvey, appointed Lumleian Lecturer in 1615, gave the lectures in which he revealed his discovery of the circulation of the blood and the methods which he used to put his theories to the proof. His first lecture was given in 1616 and this has been looked upon as the date of his discovery, but recent research by Gweneth Whitteridge, one of the few people who can read Harvey's abominable writing, sometimes in Latin, sometimes in English, has shown by a careful examination of his lecture notes and the additions he made to them from time to time, that the theory and proof of the circulation were evolving slowly in Harvey's mind over a number of years. His book, *Exercitatio anatomica de motu cordis et sanguinis*, was published in 1628 and is a masterpiece of scientific method, fit reading for any young man who is setting out on a career of research and discovery today.

Harvey was not only a great innovator but also a great benefactor to the college. He added a library to the new building (which in fact was not new, but an old building adapted for the college's purpose) and before he died in 1657 he left his patrimonial estate at Burmarsh in Kent to the college, with an exhortation to the fellows 'to search and study out the secrets of nature by way of experiment'. He left money for the holding of an annual feast to be preceded by an oration in Latin. The feast and the oration are still held, though the Latin tongue is no longer used. I would say that there have been long periods in the college history in which it has been more interested in examinations and in maintaining the dignity and prestige of the physicians than in searching and studying out the secrets of nature.

Only nine years after Harvey's death the whole of the college building including Harvey's library was destroyed by the Fire of London. The librarian, Christopher Merret, and the beadle had only been able to remove a few of the treasures—the charters, the four volumes of annals, the silver caduceus of John Caius and the portrait of Harvey, which is still to be found in the library of the present college—to a place of safety. About 140 books were also saved and a few other possessions of less note.

The Plague of London had occurred the year before, in 1665. Some physicians and apothecaries stayed in London, serving as best they could, and several of them died. The college was called upon to give advice, but many of the fellows were criticized for fleeing to the country, returning to London only when the plague had died out. Before we think too ill of them we have to remember that they were entirely dependent on their private practices which were amongst the prosperous merchants and noblemen of the City. These had already fled the town almost without exception (save the King himself) and it was the physician's job to be where his clients needed him. Within the limited social conscience of the day, and taking into account how little could then be done either to cure or to avert the infection, arrangements for the treatment of the suffering and dying populace were made as adequately as one could expect in the circumstances.

Later in the century several notable physicians were Fellows of the newly-founded Royal Society, Sir George Ent, Richard Lower and Thomas Willis amongst them, and later (in 1727), Sir Hans Sloane was to be the only person ever to be President of the Royal College of Physicians and President of the Royal

Society simultaneously. But in the late seventeenth and eighteenth centuries the college was better known for the great men who practised medicine than for any part which it played in the advancement of scientific knowledge. To some extent this only reflected the spirit of the time and one must not forget that the great practitioners of medicine, starting perhaps with Sydenham and including such personalities as John Radcliffe, Richard Mead and William Heberden, created a new era in medicine by discarding the old authoritarian practice and returning, like Hippocrates, to the bedside, to observe, record and teach.

This was what medicine needed at the time, even more than Harvey's discovery, which, it was said, had 'seemed to illuminate the theories of Medicine, yet it made no improvement in the practice thereof'. John Aubrey in Harvey's own time thought him a great man, but not a great doctor: 'All his profession would allow him to be an excellent Anatomist, but I never heard of any that admired his therapeutic way.' Harvey, like many other great men, was ahead of his time, even though the truth of his discovery was acknowledged by most physicians before he died.

The great physicians of the eighteenth century were followed by Bright and Addison—to mention only two—in the nineteenth, and they were perhaps early pioneers of the new medicine based on a sound knowledge of pathology gained from the post mortem room, and later to be based on the discoveries of the physiologists and the bacteriologists of the late nineteenth century.

Meanwhile a new college building, still in the City near to St Paul's, had been built in Warwick Lane to the plans of Robert Hooke, though it is said that Wren played some part in them. This served the college for about 150 years. However, the main centre of London society, and with it the main centre of professional interest for the physicians, was moving west, and a new college of great dignity (and inconvenience) was built in the north-west corner of Trafalgar Square, to the design of Robert Smirke, and opened in 1825. The president, Sir

Henry Halford, gave an inaugural oration in Latin in the presence of five Royal Highnesses, five Dukes including Wellington, and many other notabilities including Sir Thomas Lawrence, President of the Royal Academy. The beautiful panelling in Spanish oak which had graced one of the rooms in the Warwick Lane building had been moved to Trafalgar Square where it covered the walls of the so-called Censors' Room, used by the president when in the college, and for committees and examinations.

Sir Henry Halford, more admired and respected than beloved it was said, holds the record for having been president for twenty-four years (and 'died in office of natural decay' according to contemporary statements). He was in his time physician to George III, George IV, William IV and Victoria. (This Royal record was to be equalled by Lord Dawson who was physician to Edward VII, George V, Edward VIII and George VI. He was president from 1931 to 1938.)

When I was a young man, Lord Dawson and Lord Horder were the two most famous physicians, for whose services wealthy patients in the provinces would pay very high fees. Horder was the more brilliant of the two, and the more likely to make the right diagnosis where others had failed, but although always genial so far as I knew him, he could be blunt to the kind of patient who wanted a great fuss rather than an astute opinion. Dawson was the more diplomatic, 'get Dawson out if you want someone to speak to the relatives' was commonly said. What I want to record is that this urbane and gracious manner tended to conceal the fact that Dawson really was a great clinician, and those who thought that he succeeded solely by the elegance of his speech were grossly underestimating his skill.

He was also the natural leader of the medical profession and played a prominent part in the organization of Medicine in the new society of our time, for instance in the formation of a Ministry of Health, in the organization of the emergency medical service during the war (although he was by then seventy-five) and in the Dawson report of 1920 which, although pigeonholed at the time, foresaw the need for a National Health Service.

Lord Moran (president 1941-50) has always been a controversial figure if only because he has tended to work behind the scenes and come out with a virtual *fait accompli*. He knew the people in Government or in the profession who had the knowledge, the originality and the fearlessness required to make them useful, and he by-passed all those who held high positions by virtue of being senior and respectable, and who were not the men of ideas. This does not make for popularity and at the time of the inauguration of the Health Service he was greatly reviled by all those who were toeing the conventional line of the B.M.A. and working up hatred against the Government in general and Aneurin Bevan in particular. Not that Moran ever politically sided with the Socialists so far as I know, but he could see that a Health Service was coming whether we liked it or not, and that a great deal of what Bevan stood for, which so angered the B.M.A., would be seen as wisdom at some future time. In my view he has been proved right. Horder, in my opinion neither politician nor statesman for all his clinical skill, took the opposite view and was strongly supported in the college by all the B.M.A. supporters. At one crucial presidential election during the height of the controversy, Moran succeeded by only a very few votes. I believe the election of Horder would have been a disaster.

As a professional man, Moran's reputation, until he became Churchill's doctor, rested more on his Deanship of St Mary's Hospital Medical School than upon the scope and size of his consulting practice. But Churchill probably chose wisely. What he needed was not someone in the forefront of medical advance, with one foot in the laboratory, but an adviser who would serve him well, accompany him on his travels and realize that at times the national need far outweighed the conventional decisions of normal medical practice. Moran had the wisdom and the personality to do all this; and in case of need, Moran, as always, would know whom to turn to.

* * *

The president of the Royal College of Physicians is elected annually on the day after Palm Sunday and the method of his election must surely be unique. The president gives his annual address to the fellows and then takes off his presidential robes and sits on a chair provided for him in the background. The senior censor now takes charge of the proceedings. No one is nominated beforehand; any fellow present—and there may be two to three hundred of them—may vote for whom he pleases provided that the person in question has been a fellow of the college for at least ten years. Voting is by ballot, the ballot papers being deposited in silver urns which are brought round by the college officers. When all the votes have been collected, the senior censor reads *aloud* the name on each ballot paper. The papers are, of course, unsigned so that the voter's name is not disclosed. If the president in office is judged to be doing good work for the college he is likely to get a very large proportion of the votes, and thus to be elected annually for five or more years, unless he makes it clear that it is not his wish to be re-elected.

Reading the votes aloud gives some indication as to who are the likely successors to the presidential chair. Even in a year where the re-election of the president is a foregone conclusion, he may get, say two hundred votes and someone else may get ten, twelve or twenty, or five, and a few people often get one vote each. (Those of suspicious mind believe that some vote for themselves in order to get their names heard.) If one person gets two-thirds or more of the total votes cast, he is immediately installed as president for the ensuing year, but if no person gets two-thirds of the votes another ballot is held and this time the voting is only between the two fellows who have received most votes in the first round.

At the time of my election in 1957 it was clear that the college should play a much bigger part in the postgraduate education of physicians than it had been doing simply by holding its higher examination (the M.R.C.P.) and by its formal lectures conducted as they were with all the formality of the nineteenth and previous centuries. It should have become an active post-graduate centre where conferences were regularly held on the growing branches of medicine and medical research. Although we went ahead with this policy even in the totally inadequate Trafalgar Square building, the need for a larger and modern building was imperative. My predecessor Lord Brain had, of course, realized the inadequacy of the present college and had, with architectural advice, prepared a scheme for building two more floors upwards on the existing building. When I saw these plans I thought them still inadequate for a college with a greatly extended fellowship and a much more active programme.

The west side of Trafalgar Square really consists of one single building, the north end of which was the Royal College of Physicians and the remainder was (and still is) Canada House (though it was originally built for the Union Club). At some time in the past there had been enquiries from Canada House as to whether the Royal College would be willing to move out of their part of the site, and for some reason these conversations had come to nothing. But it so happened that there was a new High Commissioner for Canada, namely the Honourable George Drew, a very fine figure of a man who could still clearly live up to the nickname he had earned many years before of 'Gorgeous George'. He came to see me and I entertained him in the Censors' Room with its seventeenth-century panelling which looked out onto Trafalgar Square. He asked me if there was any chance of the Royal College of Physicians moving to another site. This seemed to me to be an opportunity which we ought not to miss, but of course I had to tell him that it would be dependent upon our finding a new site and having the money to build on it. I also told him at our first meeting that if we did move we should take the panelling with us.

The transaction was not a simple one for the college was not ours to sell. We had it on a peppercorn rent from George IV dating, I think, from 1826, for 999 years, but we could neither sell it nor could we let it to another user. It is important to understand this because I think there were fellows of the college who thought that we could have sold this building in the centre of London for a fabulous sum, but in fact all we could do was to ask Canada how big a consideration they would give us if we surrendered our lease to the Sovereign. This, of course, would not have been any use to them unless they had a clear understanding that when we gave up the lease they would be allowed to take over the building.

In all that followed I had the untiring help of my friend the Treasurer, Dr R. R. Bomford, and the loyal support of Sir Harold Boldero, who was then registrar of the college. We went to one of the best known valuers and estate agents who recommended that we ought to ask a sum of approximately £275,000. Dr Bomford and I thought that in view of the fact that it was greatly to the advantage of Canada that they should take over our building we ought to ask for rather more. We suggested £375,000 but Mr Drew had no mandate to go further than £325,000. Someone suggested that we might go to Sir Edward Peacock and put the facts before him. Sir Edward seemed a very suitable person as he was greatly respected in financial circles, having been a director of the Bank of England for twenty years, and was also a Canadian by origin and likely to be trusted by both sides. Dick Bomford and I went to see him and he did, in fact, advise Canada to pay £375,000, which they did.

If we were lucky in being able to dispose of our premises to such a willing buyer we were even luckier in finding our new site in Regent's Park which was very nearly ideal for our purpose. An architect, of course, had to be appointed, and we set up a committee of about twelve fellows of various ages, including one of the youngest fellows, and some who had a particular interest in art and architecture.

We very soon decided that, in the 1960s, it would be wrong to build a major London building as an imitation of a building of a former age. I went to see Lord Holford (then Sir William Holford) and Sir John Summerson and both agreed that we must have a modern building, that we should have an architect who was still in his forties and that we should not put it up to competition.

I was interested and somewhat surprised at the last piece of advice, but as they pointed out if you put the design up to competition you are bound to appoint a judge and at the end of it you may not agree with his judgment that the building is what you want and what you need. So, with further advice, we decided to interview five architects who seemed to be likely candidates; from these we picked with little hesitation Denys Lasdun, and never had reason to regret our choice. I asked him if he could build a modern building with grace, elegance and charm, which he said he could, and whether it mattered that it would be surrounded by Nash buildings in Regent's Park. He pointed out that those near neighbours, the Fellows' Building and King's College Chapel did not clash although their respective styles of architecture were some two hundred years apart.

Lasdun took endless care in studying the functions, customs and ceremonies of the college and examining also its portraits and other possessions, but when his plans were nearing completion and a model of the new college had been made, I had to get the approval of Comitia (the governing body of the fellows) to proceed and knew that there might be a good deal of opposition to such a modern building.

I explained, of course, how the committee had come to its various decisions, the great faith which we had in Denys Lasdun, and that we were all convinced that an imitation of some old building was not what we wanted. I said that I knew there were some who just did not like modern architecture at all. I then suggested that when we put it to the vote, they might look at it in this way: 'If you don't like the new building and you know what you would rather have, you must vote against it, but if you don't like the new building and you have no idea what you would put in its place, it might be more appropriate to abstain.' At this point one senior fellow made a gracious bow to the president and withdrew. The motion to proceed with the new college was carried *nem con*.

Although the college had considerable assets as well as the money which was to come from Canada House it was by now clear that the cost of the new college, if we were to build one worthy of our traditions and of the Regent's Park site, was going to be very considerable, and that even if we could afford to build it we might not be able to pay the greatly increased expenses of a much larger and more active college. The fellows themselves of course contributed generously to the new building, but having been fortunate over Canada and the site, we now had the greatest good fortune of all in the gift of £500,000 from the Wolfson Foundation. It is to be hoped that all the new fellows who now enjoy the building realize that it was this magnificent gift which really made our venture possible, and I am glad to record here my personal gratitude. On 6 March 1962 the foundation stone was laid by the Queen Mother.

My years as President of the Royal College of Physicians were full of interest, especially to myself. Above all, the opportunity of getting to know the great majority of the physicians of this country was unique, and I have many memories of the contacts I made, both within and without the profession of Medicine. A five-year presidency I judged to be enough. Another three years would have been needed to see us into the new college which was opened by the Queen on 5 November 1964.

11. The Cigarette

A chapter on the cigarette comes suitably as an appendix of sorts to one on the Royal College of Physicians, as it was in 1962, during my presidency, that we published the first College report on Smoking and Health.

The idea that we should do this was put to me by Dr Charles Fletcher. I readily consented and we set up a strong committee which met regularly for about two years, our task being not to do research, but to study the already overwhelming evidence incriminating the cigarette as a cause of illness, and put it together in a form which the intelligent layman could read and understand. In an attempt to avoid undue bias we had two heavy cigarette smokers on the committee; they both gave up smoking before we had finished examining the evidence. The College has recently issued its second report on the subject. In the meantime the Surgeon General of the U.S.A. has issued a similar report.

The Medical Research Council and the Ministry of Health have repeatedly drawn attention to the health hazards of smoking. These various reports describe the evidence in some detail, and give its sources. Much of the evidence is of course statistical and therefore boring to some, but most decisions on which action has to be taken (such as alcohol and traffic accidents) is of a statistical nature. All I shall try to do here is to highlight the facts which I think are most important and about which no reasonable person can any longer be in doubt.

First and foremost, cigarette smoking is an addiction, and an extremely powerful one. As soon as a young person has started to smoke regularly, even if at first it is only furtively in the school basement or lavatories, he is likely to be hooked and to find it difficult and in many cases almost impossible to give up.

The pharmacological facts still need some elucidation, if only because cigarette smoke is an extremely complex substance containing numerous different chemicals, but the evidence seems to point to nicotine as being the ingredient most responsible for the addiction, that is the drug-dependence, whereas the tar which results from the burning of the tobacco leaf is mostly responsible for the development of lung cancer. The irritant qualities of the inhaled smoke are probably responsible for the cough and for chronic bronchitis (and its sequel, emphysema, which eventually destroys the lungs) whereas the nicotine may be the factor responsible for the greatly increased incidence of coronary heart disease in cigarette smokers. Those who inhale the smoke from cigarettes get more nicotine into their system more quickly than those who use tobacco in any other way, and are therefore most exposed to its ill effects and also most addicted.

It must of course be noted that as with certain other addictive drugs such as the amphetamines, the barbiturates and alcohol, there are some people who can use the drug in strict moderation, but whereas with alcohol these are the majority, with cigarette smoking they are the exception, and these moderate smokers usually do not inhale. They run no great risk except to others, for they tend to spread the view that anyone can smoke in moderation if they try. That this is not so is shown by the fact that in 1968 77 per cent of male smokers (but only 25 per cent of women) said that they inhaled.

At all ages fewer women smoke fewer cigarettes than men, and whereas 83 per cent of male smokers started before they were twenty years old only 60 per cent of women smokers did. The majority of addicted male smokers smoke more than 15 cigarettes daily, many of them 25 or over. A few smoke 30 to 50. In recent years cigarette smoking amongst men has slightly fallen whereas in women it has increased. Because of these differences between the sexes it is no surprise to learn that the diseases common to smokers are much less frequent in women, but are steadily increasing; this is especially true of lung cancer.

The cigarette manufacturers must be aware of this, and it

will be noted that as most men already smoke, and as the habit is a powerful addiction readily acquired in youth, if you really want to increase your profits and are brutally indifferent to causing cancer of the lung (a hideous and fatal disease) in women as well as men, the most effective thing is to design advertisements which picture glamorous young ladies smoking cigarettes. That was precisely what the cigarette manufacturers were doing early in 1971. I wrote a pretty strong letter about it to *The Times* and was gratified to note that the beautiful young ladies disappeared in a few weeks. Now the manufacturers are trying more subtle ways of enticing young women into the net: beautiful female hands holding a slim cigarette are currently to be seen in the Underground advertisements and elsewhere.

In 1962, the date of the first College report, the manufacturers were spending £11·3 million annually in various forms of advertising. In 1968 they spent the equivalent of £37·5 million (actually 52·2 million adjusted to 37·5 to make a fair comparison allowing for the increased cost of advertising). During the same period those engaged in other trades (cosmetics for instance) also increased their advertising but not nearly to the same extent.

The latest figures available to me for deaths from cancer of the lung (almost wholly attributable to cigarette smoking) in the United Kingdom were 26,973 males and 5,565 females. This was in the year 1968. It is more than four times the deaths from traffic accidents. About 15,000 of these deaths occurred between the ages of 35 and 64.

But this of course is less than half the story. Lung cancer takes pride of place because it is a horrible, inexorable and pitiless disease. In terms of actual numbers, excess deaths from coronary heart disease and chronic bronchitis due to smoking kill more people than cancer. By excess deaths we mean that the connexion between coronary heart disease and cigarette smoking is not so close as between lung cancer and smoking. A fair number of non-smokers die of coronary heart disease though very few of lung cancer, so we can only speak of the excess of deaths as being attributable to the cigarette.

Because cigarette smoking is such a powerful addiction and many smokers find it difficult or impossible to give up, they naturally try to justify themselves and prefer not to face too many of the facts. The first defence is usually: 'Well most of these deaths are in old people. I don't want to live too long. You've got to die of something.' The facts do not support this. If you take men of 35 who are non-smokers, 82 per cent can expect to live to be 65 or over. If you take smokers of 15-24 cigarettes at age 35, only 69 per cent will live to be 65, and only 60 per cent of those who smoke 25 or more a day. These surely are striking figures. The deaths increase from 35 onwards. Non-smokers have only a 1 in 75 chance of dying in the decade 35 to 44 but heavy smokers have a 1 in 10 chance of dying during those years. A great many of the deaths in the younger age groups are the result of premature coronary artery disease.

The next defence is: 'It's too late to give up now, I've smoked for so many years.' This too is untrue. British doctors heeding the warning which should be clear to all have so altered their smoking habits in recent years that their death rate from lung cancer has substantially fallen, while it has continued to rise in the general population. After ten years of non-smoking the life expectancy will have returned to near normal.

The next defences have a little more support in fact, namely that the cigarette gives the smoker pleasure and in some cases is claimed to calm his nerves. This of course is true of any addiction, for in acquiring an addiction you acquire a new craving and only when that craving is satisfied are you back to what is, for you, a state of normality. The heroin addict just cannot bear life without heroin, but, surely no one would therefore argue that heroin is something which we all need and is good for us. In fact most of those who have successfully given up smoking will tell you that after getting over the initial period of unsatisfied craving, which can last for several weeks, and can be intense and well-nigh intolerable, you feel not only better in health and physical fitness (cough and breathlessness soon disappear) but also that you feel calmer and much more able to face difficult personal contacts without giving in to nerves and fumbling urgently for the cigarettes and the matches. And of course the reformed smoker can, if he wishes, easily, if rather wickedly, put the visiting smoker at a disadvantage by not having any ashtrays or offering any cigarettes.

Putting on weight is another excuse for not giving up smoking and it is quite true that to give up smoking and avoid indulging the appetite at the same time is indeed hard. The final reason, usually for starting again after a few days abstinence, is 'My wife says I'm too irritable.' This is really very transparent. There must be few wives, if they are not smokers themselves, who wouldn't be willing to exert a little patience, for the rewards are great and rapid. Apart from the husband's health, the sheer saving on the weekly budget is colossal over the years, and to have rooms fragrant with fresh flowers instead of stale smoke, and to be freed from those filthy ashtrays and the cigarette burns on the mantelpiece, carpets and elsewhere are very real gains. To go to bed with someone whose breath, hair, body and clothes do not reek of tobacco must also be quite an advantage.

As an ex-addict I must offer a little advice to those many smokers who really wish they could give up. Don't think it is going to be easy. There is no easy way (though some heavily addicted smokers find it very much easier than they anticipated). Prepare for a few days of intense craving and misery, spread out to a few weeks of less acute distress; choose a holiday to start the process, when you can get out to enjoy the fresh air and the newly discovered scent of the countryside, and when you will have time to argue with yourself, aloud if need be. When you are busy and harassed it is all too easy to throw resolution to the winds and accept the first cigarette offered. Above all, having given up, don't say 'I've lost the craving now, I'll just enjoy a cigarette occasionally.' You will be smoking twenty a day within a few weeks.

And now a word about finance and the Government. The annual revenue from tobacco is, I believe about £1,100 million. It is said that no Government could afford to lose such a revenue. This is nonsense. The cigarette addiction is so strong that the chance of millions of smokers suddenly giving up is negligible.

The process is bound to be only a very gradual one during which other sources of revenue would be found. In the long run the nation would be better off as tobacco is one of our largest imports. There would also be an enormous saving of working days now lost through illnesses such as bronchitis and coronary heart disease, and of the expense of looking after these invalids, and paying their sickness benefit. This you may say would be temporary. Everyone dies eventually, more would live into old age; but the cost of seeing an old person through his last illness is much less demanding of public funds than the intensive care units for coronary disease and the operations and radiation treatment of lung cancer.

What should we all, including the Government, do? First, abolish the evil propaganda and advertising of the cigarette manufacturers. Develop and spread an attitude of contempt for them. Abolish the sale of cigarettes (readily available to children) from vending machines. Encourage the development of facilities everywhere on transport and in public places for non-smokers. Gradually work towards a society which regards smoking as something abnormal, something we tolerate but find rather dirty and distasteful. Above all *never* encourage, by word, deed or example, the development of the addiction in young people.

12. A Note on Statistics

I have often wanted to say something about statistics (I never quite know whether it's 'them' or 'it'; even Fowler [see '-ics 2'] doesn't help me very much) because I think that, like policemen and mathematics, whether you like them (it) or not depends on an attitude of mind. A great deal of nonsense is written about statistics, and statistical fallacies; of course it *is* possible to make mistakes by adding up figures wrongly or using inappropriate mathematical techniques, but ninety-nine times out of a hundred a statistical fallacy, like a computer mistake, is due not to the method or the machine but to the person who uses it.

The first thing to grasp is that there is nothing odd or sinister about them. In a sense we use statistical methods every day in making quite ordinary decisions in that we are applying data assembled by past observations as a means of predicting the probable future. For instance 'if I go out to the shops now am I more, or less, likely to meet Mrs Skeggs (whom I don't like) than if I go in an hour's time?' is a question which can only be answered statistically, the decision being based upon numerical observation of Mrs Skeggs's habits converted roughly (by the human computer) into terms of statistical probability. If her habits are fairly regular the decision may be a near certainty; if less regular, only a greater or lesser likelihood can be predicted. The 'scatter' (the statistician would say) is greater and a far longer period of observation would be necessary. Most data can be roughly quantified in this way, as very likely, probable, or unpredictable.

To turn now to medicine, instead of saying 'I think Treatment A is better than Treatment B' we can do an experiment comparing two series of cases given treatments A and B respectively, 'limiting the variables', as we say, by matching the two groups as far as possible by age, sex and social class. From the results we can measure (i.e. count) the number of cases in which Treatment A fails where B succeeds or vice versa. We may have to consider how to quantify what we call failure or success, for instance by counting the deaths in serious disease, or by recording the number of days of fever in an infectious illness.

Then we need some measure of whether the, perhaps slight, difference between the two groups is really due to pure chance, for no two such groups would behave in exactly the same way even if they both had identical treatment or no treatment at all. The statisticians can work out for us, by clever mathematical devices which you and I need not learn, the likelihood of any event having taken place by chance, and this is usually expressed in terms of 'statistical significance'.

To take the most elementary example, if you pick out a card from a pack the likelihood of getting a red card three times running is one in eight (i.e. 2^3 as there are three tries and two alternatives at each try). The likelihood of getting five red cards running is one in 2^5 or 1 in 32. At that degree of significance or unlikeliness we might suspect some hanky panky was going on, that some element other than chance was at work. The chance of ten red cards running is one in 2^{10} (1024), and were this to happen you would readily be convinced that you were not being exposed to fair play. (In this example we suppose the card is put back in the pack after each draw, otherwise the number of available red cards would progressively diminish.)

In judging trials of treatment we often take one in twenty (P, or probability $= 0.05$) as our criterion. If P is less than this we think it reasonable to assume that we are witnessing a real difference and not a chance result, and that it is 'statistically significant'. But this is a purely arbitrary choice, and what we ought to say is that it is 'significant at the 5% level' or $P = 0.05$. Where there is a powerful influence at work, P is sometimes less than 0.001 (likelihood of a purely chance result less than one in a thousand) and of course we are then readily convinced that we are witnessing a real phenomenon. But we can never say it could never have happened by chance (i.e. $P = 0$), and you must remember that if you do enough trials one will turn up by pure chance.

Take the likelihood of a family of six children all being boys. This is approximately one in sixty-four (assuming the sex ratio in live births to be about equal), but there must be thousands of families in Britain with six children. If there are 6,400 such families, a hundred of them should consist of six boys, so that in itself does not prove that there is anything peculiar about the parentage of such a family. Only were we to find that in a large population the number of six-child families with six boys was *significantly greater* than one in sixty-four would we begin to wonder if the parents were unable to have girl-children. No such case ever seems to have been convincingly made out.

As we have seen, one purpose and use of statistics in medicine is to use the statistical data with a view to predicting the future, so that we can guide the course of illness as far as this is possible. For instance, should we advise immediate surgery for a patient bleeding internally from a duodenal ulcer? It is known that operations are more risky in older people (though not so much as they used to be) but on the other hand the chances of dying of the haemorrhage without operation are much higher as age advances over about forty years.

This knowledge has been gained by the careful collection of statistics. (The actual decision would not be made on this evidence alone but it is very important knowledge to have.) Statistical methods are also used in the testing of new remedies as in our example of Treatment A versus Treatment B.

But statistics may (and often do) throw up new lines of thought which can lead to major discoveries. The fact that heavy cigarette smokers are some forty times more likely to develop lung cancer than non-smokers is one of the most important medical discoveries of our time. Or statistics can put us on to new lines of enquiry. The fact that women over about fifty have a far better life expectancy than men needs explanation, though there is unlikely to be a single cause for this.

There are also some so-called statistical fallacies. The most irritating habit of persons who have never been taught to think scientifically—or perhaps to think at all—is what one might call 'the fallacy of my wife's aunt'. Having tried patiently to explain that the evidence of a (presumably causative) connexion between cigarette smoking and lung cancer is very strong indeed so strong that about one in eight of heavy cigarette smokers dies of the disease, you are immediately told 'my wife's aunt used to smoke cigarettes and lived to be ninety'. It is quite infuriating; obviously she had a seven to one chance of escaping as, in fact, you have just explained. For some reason the exact opposite seems to be the response to a discussion of motor accidents. No one says 'but my wife's aunt drove a car and didn't die of a traffic accident'. They say 'everyone seems to be having motor accidents'. In fact lung cancer causes at least four times the deaths due to traffic accidents in England and Wales. There is no excuse for this kind of misunderstanding of statistics. No mathematical knowledge is needed at this level nor is it needed in the other examples I shall give which show the importance of correct interpretation of statistical data. All are real instances, though I have not checked dates and figures where they are not necessary to the argument.

The Registrar-General's figures for 1930-32 showed that angina pectoris (a term then used for many deaths which would now be described as due to coronary thrombosis or myocardial infarction) was much commoner in Social Class I (professional workers) than in Class V (unskilled workers). Was this due to the stresses and strains of life in the executive class, or to lack of exercise? Or what? I pointed out that the deaths from 'myocarditis' showed just the opposite tendency. (Myocarditis was a loose old-fashioned term still in use at that time for heart failure not due to valvular disease.) It seemed to me probable that those in Social Class I would have up-to-date doctors and the advice of consultants, and that the apparent distinction between classes might not be a real one at all, but due to an outdated nomenclature more often used on the death certificates of Social Class V. This was considerably borne out by later figures which showed that the difference between the classes in 1951 was less than two to one instead of four to one as had at first appeared.

Some time ago certain workers supported by the Medical Research Council made the interesting observation that leukaemia and other types of malignant disease were more likely to arise in the summer months than at other times of the year. This seemed an interesting phenomenon worthy of full-scale investigation, until I suggested that it was probably because family doctors went on holiday in the summer months. There is nothing that a new doctor likes better than to find something that his predecessor has missed. To the regular doctor the patient was only too familiar; the idea penetrated slowly that he was in fact now commencing with a new disease. Moreover the locum doctor would often be a young man fresh from hospital where serious disease is common (perhaps he was earning extra money in his vacation) and he would be more on the look out for early cancer in his patients. I do not know what finally became of this observation.

The excessive death rate from bronchitis in miners is interesting. Its cause seems obvious until you find almost the same excess in coal-miners' wives. Clearly we have a more complex situation than at first appears.

The cure of cancer is an uncertain matter. It may recur in a few months after an operation to remove the primary growth, or in one, two or more years, or not at all. As one cannot wait an indefinite time before trying to assess the results of treatment it is therefore common and convenient to refer to '5-year survivals' which are roughly equivalent to cures. And if one method, say irradiation, gives a better 5-year survival than another method (say surgery) in cases which are comparable with regard to site and pathology, that is considered evidence that the method is superior. But the same method of appraisal was applied erroneously to test the value of *early* treatment in cancer of the breast. It showed that cases which came to operation early in the disease were more likely to survive for five years or more. While it is no doubt true that earlier diagnosis increases the chance of cure, this is a fallacious way of measuring the results. Why? Suppose that in cancer of the breast the date of onset could be accurately determined, and all cases survived for six years exactly, with or without treatment. Those that were seen by the surgeon in the first year of their disease would all be alive five years later even if no treatment were given at all, and those first seen in the third year of illness would all be dead.

One of the most troublesome and common causes of fallacy in statistical interpretation is due to the two populations compared not being really similar in some important respect. A dangerous comparison was made in 1957 between the mortality due to certain 'surgical' diseases such as prostatic disease and appendicitis, in teaching and non-teaching hospitals, to the detriment of the latter. But, as I pointed out, anyone in a large university town like Manchester knows that there is an important social difference between patients in the two types of hospital, the teaching hospitals attracting a larger number of those who would be likely to have better nutrition and higher intelligence leading to early and efficient medical aid.

But the best example I know of the fallacy of drawing conclusions by comparing data from dissimilar populations, or by expressing the data in the wrong terms, concerns the deaths of radiologists. A good many years ago it was discovered that the average age at death of radiologists was some ten to fifteen years less than that of physicians. The interesting thing was that all the usual causes of death contributed to the mortality; it was not particularly noticeable in deaths from leukaemia or cancer which might have been due to radiation. This was very mysterious and very disconcerting.

Fortunately the solution was soon found. Radiology was a relatively new and rapidly growing speciality. Consequently there *were* no old radiologists (or only very few of them) living into the years of senility. Those that had died had therefore died at fifty to sixty rather than seventy to eighty as was the case for many of their physician colleagues. The average age at death was therefore much less. Had the result been expressed in terms of the likelihood of death occurring in radiologists of say fifty to sixty as compared with physicians of *similar age* there would have been no significant discrepancy.

A similar fallacy occurred many years ago when the proportions of infant deaths due to tuberculous meningitis showed an alarming rise. This was due to the prevention of diphtheria from which so many infants had previously died. The actual number of deaths from tuberculous meningitis was unchanged, but the *proportion* of all infant deaths due to this cause had of course increased.

Finally one must guard against the fallacy of two factors being related. There is for instance a considerable correlation between smoking and alcohol consumption, the heavy drinker being often a heavy smoker. So perhaps the lung cancer deaths are after all due to alcohol? This can be tested and disproved by separating the two factors and constructing a two by two table. In each square we put the number of cases and the death rate from lung cancer:

	Smoking high	Smoking low
Alcohol high	1 Many cases high death rate	2 Few cases low death rate
Alcohol low	3 Fewer cases but high death rate	4 Many cases low death rate

In modern methods of medicine the science of statistics has often occur together but it is the exceptions in squares 2 and 3 that show conclusively that it is the cigarette that is at work in lung cancer. If the correlation between the two habits were very close, it might be difficult to get sufficient of the exceptions (in squares 2 and 3) which prove the rule.

In modern methods of medicine the science of statistics has added much to the accuracy with which we can judge the results of treatment and the validity of some of our hypotheses, but the great therapeutic victories such as the cure of tuberculosis, the prevention of malaria or the operation for mitral stenosis do not require statistical validation before we believe what we can see so clearly through our own unaided senses. I am therefore some-what concerned lest the extreme believer in the creed of scientific medicine should be bringing up a generation of doctors who can no longer trust their own observations or their judgment. If so they will lack an appreciation of the greatest of human qualities.

In preparation for this coming generation much of great literature will have to be rewritten, else it will be incomprehensible. Always willing to be at the forefront of any new movement I have made a start on *Julius Caesar*:

> Computers which have captured from the stars
> Their role of prophecy, discern a link
> 'Twixt body-weight and loyalty, such that P
> Is meaningful at less than point-nought-five.
> Thus would I have about me men,
> More to the right of distribution curves
> Than yond lean Cassius. He thinks too much
> Statistic'ly such men are dangerous.*

* Quoted in an article in *The British Medical Journal* 8.3.69, p. 636.

13. The House of Lords

It is a characteristic of the human mind that memories of the past, experiences of the present and anticipations of the future are overlaid by some affective quality which makes them pleasant or unpleasant, exciting or dull, or endowed with some kind of patina of quiet satisfaction, or of fear and anxiety, or of challenge, so that one meets them to some extent prepared. It is a mistake to be too logical and to think you like something for this reason or that. The human computer has already worked it out for you and is several moves ahead; only later do you begin to analyse the reasons. And if at this stage I pause to consider why I like the House of Lords, many reasons come to mind; but how many are good reasons I do not know. Of course it is nice to receive a letter from the Prime Minister signed in his own hand which says 'I have it in mind to submit your name to the Queen with the recommendation that Her Majesty may be graciously pleased to approve that the dignity of a Barony of the United Kingdom for Life be conferred upon you ...' but however gratifying this may be to personal vanity it does not of itself make for lasting satisfaction.

We do not really have to look far to see some of the merits of the Upper House. It is an assembly, surely unique amongst political institutions, of people who are expert in a hundred different ways. It is, I suppose, fashionable in these days of democracy to ascribe this to the advent and influence of the life peers, but this would be a mistaken view. It is true that the life peers have brought a new element of expertise into the House and, as many of them sit on the cross-benches, the House is less politically divided than it was, but those hereditary peers who make it their duty to attend regularly (and there are many of them) include many persons of astute mind, great culture and vast experience. Many have filled important government posts at home or abroad, others are from long-established land-owning families who bring to the House an interest in agriculture and related problems which helps to save us from the present-day domination of industry and science. And by the accident of an early death in the family there are amongst them a number of very able young men who would hardly be eligible yet for a life peerage.

Some say that the House of Lords is the best club in the world, and certainly it is a clubby place containing numerous 'clubbable people', to use Johnson's phrase. But it is so much more than a club, for we all have a common interest in government, legislation and current affairs and intelligent pursuits even if we do not all agree on how these affairs should be conducted (and how dull it would be if we did). (Some call the Athenaeum the second-best club, but if so it stands a long way behind because of its steadfast and out-dated exclusion of women members.)

In addition to all this, the House of Lords has the great advantage of not being a democratic institution. Perhaps I should explain myself in a little more detail. Most of my friends know that my politics are left of centre, that is, I find myself usually more in alignment with the ideals of the radicals and the socialists than I do with the hypocrisy of the Tory Party. The reader does not need to have an exceptional degree of discernment to note that my choice of antithesis does not suggest an entirely neutral political attitude. But I sit on the cross-benches because I think that in the House of Lords I speak for Medicine and not for one political party or another and I welcome the right to disagree with the Government or with the Opposition without party allegiance.

I have described myself as a Socialist who believes in privilege (though I think you should earn it and not buy it) and as a Socialist who does not believe in majority rule. Carried to the extreme, majority rule would give us football, boxing (and probably public executions) but no chamber music. I also claim to be a human biologist and as such I see not only people and animals and plants, but also ethics and social customs as the products of thousands of years of evolution. I know of no animal society and no human society for that matter, which by a process of evolution has arrived at true majority rule and certainly I know of no society which is egalitarian in any true sense of the word. All societies have their leaders. Imagine how chaotic would be the migration of birds if its timing and direction relied on a majority vote.

The virtue of democracy is two-fold: it is a protection against tyranny and as a system it tends to throw up leaders who are bound to have some respect for the needs of the people. Even here it fails, as we know only too well. Any measure requiring the slightest degree of self-discipline, so that the nation as a whole shall benefit in the long run, is liable to lead to the rapid downfall of the Government and its replacement by the opposite party, however inept its policy may be, however transparent its hypocrisy, and however brittle its promises. The House of Lords, on the other hand, can debate issues of the greatest social importance without relevance to a majority vote.

As a human biologist interested in selective breeding I also see some of the advantages of the hereditary principle. I am, alas, not one of those who can describe himself as the third son of the eighth Marquis of Kenilworth, and I admit to being mildly envious of those who can so describe themselves. What have they done to deserve it? Absolutely nothing. What have I done to deserve my inheritance from my own forbears of a more than ordinary ability to achieve some of the ambitions with which I have been endowed? Absolutely nothing.

There is much to be said for a mixture of hereditary and life peers. The disadvantage of the life peers is that if they are given their peerage relatively early in their careers, shall we say at the age of fifty, they are still so active in their own professions or other activities that they cannot spare time to attend the House of Lords except when there is some matter being discussed which is in their particular field of knowledge and expertise. For this reason I am very much against the idea current in the recent attempt to reform the House of Lords that unless there is a certain minimal attendance peers should not be amongst the voting peers, that is, they would have the privilege of sitting in the House but not recording their vote. This, I think, is completely wrong. If we have amongst the peers a certain number who are profoundly competent to speak, shall we say, for science, scientific discovery and scientific education, and these are moreover people who are still active in the world of science, it is ridiculous to bring in some rule whereby they may not vote because they have not made a certain number of attendances. We should not require them to put in an attendance, for the sake of doing so, while the 'Street Offences Bill' or the 'Rural Water Supplies and Sewerage (Scotland) Bill' are being debated. If, alternatively, the life peerage is granted to people as the final crowning honour of a successful career (successful, we presume, from the point of view of their contribution to the welfare of others as well as their own personal success), then we are in danger of creating a house full of old men. People will get the life peerage, as I did, at the age of sixty-seven and within a few years will be in their seventies—still useful, we hope, but no longer at the forefront of new knowledge.

I look towards a society which is based more and more on equality of opportunity, and to that extent the hereditary peerage is an anachronism, but I do not look towards a society which makes its decisions on a show of hands, because I know that new ideas, whether in science, politics or music come from individuals or from minorities.

It remains for me to comment on some of the more intimate and endearing qualities of the House of Lords. That the Room which would normally be labelled 'Gentlemen' is appropriately labelled 'Peers' is only one indication of the atmosphere of the place. The staff are superb. Everyone seems to know your name, how they do it I cannot think. And this goes throughout. Whether you visit the Chief Whip's Office or the Hansard Office or whether one of the attendants has a telephone message for you, or whether you go for a drink, everyone seems to know your name and treat you with just a little respect which in no way precludes a conversation on friendly and personal terms.

The day after I was introduced to the House, I went to the bar to get a drink before lunch. The barmaid very politely said to me 'You are a peer, are you not?' 'I am,' I replied, 'but you may well ask, because I was only introduced to the House yesterday.' 'Oh, then,' was her immediate response, 'you're either Lord Platt or Lord Jackson.' (Willis Jackson was introduced to the House on the same day.)

After a meeting of the Clinical Research Board of the Medical Research Council (of which I was then Chairman), I lunched at the House of Lords, where, during the afternoon, I was going to oppose the Archbishop of Canterbury on an amendment to the Abortion Bill. It happened that I sat next to the Bishop of Chester, and I said to him 'Believe it or not I have just come from the Medical Research Council where the last decision I had to make was on an application for the support of research into the behaviour of primates.' The Bishop rose to the occasion and commented, 'It shouldn't take very long, there are only two of them.'

I am convinced that the archaic formalities of speech which are still adhered to in the House of Lords are an important factor in keeping the debates at a high level, for they lead to masterpieces of understatement and avoid personal wrangling and abuse. Sometimes it seems almost a challenge to see how rude one can be while still referring to one's opponent as 'The Noble and Learned Viscount': 'I thank the Noble Lord for his courteous reply to my question which I must say I find completely unhelpful' is a good example of the approved style of address. Its very formality is its virtue, and we must not take too seriously the fact that the appellation 'Noble and Gallant Lord' may only be used of Peers who hold the rank of Admiral of the Fleet, Field Marshal, or Marshal of the Royal Air Force. The award of a Victoria Cross does not entitle one to this particular form of address.

Much as I dislike the worst excesses of democracy, a democratic government is a safeguard against other and worse forms of government, and I therefore think it right that the powers of the House of Lords should be limited, as indeed they are. The composition of the House should be revised by a gradual process, the hereditary element becoming less important, but I have given my reasons for thinking that a complete change-over would not be beneficial. Moreover, I think it is absurd to curtail the powers of the House of Lords still further while at the same time reforming its composition. Surely we should either have a reformed House of Lords with more powers, or an illogical House of Lords with its present powers.

At present we are important in many respects: as a revising chamber, amending legislation which reaches us ill-considered from 'another place', as a debating chamber where issues of great social importance may be discussed without reference to being popular or unpopular with the electorate; as a chamber where private members' bills have more chance of promotion than in the Commons; as a society which contains very many wise and distinguished men who would not enter the contest for a seat in the Commons; as an institution which preserves some of the best traditions of British Society, and can, now and then, restrain some of democracy's worst stupidities.

It has been a surprise to me to find how many topics are debated in the Lords with which, as a doctor, one is bound to be particularly concerned. Euthanasia, divorce, animal experiment, abortion, smoking, boxing, alcohol and driving, bronchitis in coal-miners, social services, and services for the chronic sick and disabled, as well as the National Health Service, have all been discussed in the last four years. But there are also topics of great importance on which one can have strong feelings even though they have no specifically medical content. The sale of arms to South Africa and the Immigration Act are examples.

There are so many common misconceptions about the House of Lords that a short statement on our methods and habits may be acceptable. Normally we sit on Tuesdays, Wednesdays and Thursdays, but when there is much parliamentary business to transact we commonly sit on Mondays as well, and sometimes Fridays. The Lord Chancellor's procession lead by the mace enters at two-thirty precisely. The doors are then closed to all strangers for about five minutes while their Lordships are at prayer. Prayers are led by one of the bishops. There is no need to attend. Many, if not most of us, wait outside the doors until prayers are over.

As you enter you bow to the throne (which of course is unoccupied). The business usually starts with questions, generally limited to four. Supplementary questions may be asked either by the original questioner or by any other peer, but they must be *questions*. One must not say 'I think it is high time that her Majesty's Government ...', but 'Is her Majesty's Government aware that the long delay is causing much concern ...'. Sometimes the exchanges between questioner and responder are witty and entertaining.

The average daily attendance at the House is 265. The numbers tail off somewhat around tea-time, then fill out again but diminish once more at six, seven or eight o'clock, depending on the importance and interest of the business. On important issues when a division is expected there may be several hundred peers present until late in the night. If we are likely to sit until nine or ten, or later, a good buffet supper is provided (not gratis of course).

Questions are often followed by short and formal items of business which do not give rise to any controversy. Then there is usually a major item which can take four or five hours at least, with a list of twenty or more speakers. This may be the second reading of an important bill which has either originated in the House of Lords or come up from 'another place'. To speak in such a debate you should put your name down beforehand, and get up to speak without prompting when your turn comes. The main spokesmen from Government or Opposition front benches will probably speak for twenty or thirty minutes. Other speakers are not welcome to speak for more than fifteen minutes, but often do. There are no rules.

The Lord Chancellor from the Woolsack puts the motion before the House but in no way takes charge. The House looks after itself, and if anyone breaks the rules, calls of 'order, order' come up from all quarters. If a tricky matter of procedure should arise, the Leader of the House (at present Earl Jellicoe) will decide upon it. If the Lord Chancellor is himself promoting a bill or speaking in debate, he moves a few paces to the left to indicate that he is no longer addressing the House officially from the Woolsack. Then he may return to the Woolsack to put the motion on which he has just been speaking.

A second-reading debate should properly confine itself to principles; to the general desirability of the legislation proposed, and not to details of the wording of clauses. This comes at the committee stage, and most committees in the Lords are committees of the whole House. In committee the rules are relaxed, you may speak more than once, and need not announce your intention beforehand.

The House of Lords is famous for another type of debate which usually takes place on a Wednesday and in which a topic of general interest and importance is discussed without any legislation being proposed and without any division being taken. Since someone must put a motion before the House in order to have a debate, the opening is usually worded in this way: 'To call attention to the present state of Northern Ireland and to move for papers.' This formality is presumably meant to be a request that relevant documents should be placed before the House, but in fact when everyone (perhaps twenty or more speakers) has had his say, the opener at the end of his winding-up speech 'begs leave to withdraw his motion' and 'the motion is by leave withdrawn'. These debates can be of value and interest, and give an opportunity for free and relaxed exchanges of view, often from exceedingly well-informed persons with no compulsion to speak from a particular party point of view, though naturally the Opposition will often be critical of the action or non-action of the Government.

As in all live societies a good deal of the life and work of the House takes place informally, in the dining-room, the bar and elsewhere. Perhaps I should also explain that we do not sit in robes and coronets! When a new peer is introduced, he and his two sponsors will be robed, otherwise (with the exception of the Lord Chancellor) peers only wear robes once a year, at the Opening of Parliament.

In conclusion let me say that whatever Government comes into power, should it attempt a really radical reform of the House of Lords, in particular by trying to make us another elected House, I hope its efforts will fail, as they have failed in the past.

14. Euthanasia

On 25 March 1969 Lord Raglan moved the second reading of his Voluntary Euthanasia Bill in the House of Lords. The debate lasted about six hours and the bill failed to get its second reading by sixty-one votes to forty, but, as many of those who opposed the bill said they were doing so not on the grounds of principle but because they thought the bill in its present form was not a good one, it seems reasonable to assume that not more than fifty per cent were opposed to the principle of euthanasia under any possible circumstances.

The subject had been discussed in the House of Lords on two previous occasions. In 1936 a bill was promoted by the late Lord Ponsonby of Sulbrede and that bill owed its conception to the late Lord Moynihan, President of the Royal College of Surgeons, but unfortunately it came before the House after his death. There was another debate on the subject, without a bill, in 1950. It is clear from the first instance that the concept of euthanasia has had the interest and approval of certain prominent members of the medical profession for at least thirty-three years.

There are three main facets to the problem: do we think that euthanasia is justifiable, humane and ethical under certain circumstances? Would we, under those circumstances want it for ourselves, and if so, what are the circumstances?

The most obvious, and I think the simplest case is that in which a person, young or old, has had his brain damaged beyond any hope of recovery (perhaps by a road accident) but can be kept in a state of suspended animation by cardiac pacemakers, breathing machines and tube feeding. In such cases, after every possible test has been done, and after full consultation, I think there is general agreement that there comes a time when the apparatus must be switched off and it is useless to go on keeping the 'person' alive. Indeed, some would say that he is already dead and many who would oppose euthanasia on religious or other grounds under all other circumstances would, I think, agree that it is right to terminate life in such cases.

The second case is that of a patient suffering from terminal illness which appears to be inevitably fatal; advanced cancer is the usual example. It is usually conceded that such patients have the right to be kept under the influence of drugs designed to relieve pain and suffering as far as it is possible and that if in some circumstances this leads to the drugs being given in doses which are bound to shorten the patient's life, then this is justifiable. A national opinion poll of a thousand doctors in January 1965 showed that seventy-six per cent agreed that medical men do in fact act in this way. It seems to me an entirely similar action if the patient under these circumstances develops pneumonia which could be controlled by antibiotics but the doctor decides against giving the antibiotic. To these two examples I would personally add a third: that in the event of the patient signifying his intention of taking an overdose of drugs to free himself of an intolerable terminal illness, I for one would not prevent him.

Some, including myself, might add a fourth example, namely that if an aged person's heart stops beating, no meddlesome person shall come along with scientific gadgets and start it again, for although there are plenty of authentic cases in which the heart has been successfully re-started in younger people, who have then made a complete recovery and gone back to a normal life, in older persons the danger of dementia following temporary arrest of the circulation to the brain is great. Old people should be allowed to die once, and not twice.

If you go with me even as far as the first two examples, then we have surely conceded that there is no absolute rule, natural or supernatural which forbids some kind of euthanasia under every possible circumstance. Consequently, this does not seem to me to justify a kind of blanket resolution such as the Central Ethical Committee of the Council of the British Medical Association has made which 'reiterates the policy of the Association that the practice of euthanasia under any circumstances be condemned'.

But this is not all. Indeed, if it were all I would wholeheartedly agree with those who hold that, whatever doctors in their own conscience decide to do under these circumstances, there is no call for legislation at the present time. This kind of euthanasia needs only negative—or at most indirect—action on the part of the doctor; he is not being asked actively to terminate the life of someone who is showing no immediate signs of dying. It is tremendously important to point this out because this aspect was continually in danger of being lost from sight in the debate in the House of Lords which centred very much on the question of the terminal care of the cancer patient.

The second situation is much more difficult and is typified by the severe stroke which renders the patient quite unable to speak, unable to attend to himself for the needs of nutrition and excretion, and unable to move in bed without assistance, yet showing absolutely no sign of dying. Such patients sometimes live on for a good many years. A similar state can arise in terminal disease of the brain and spinal cord. The bill provided for those who feel, as I do, that they should be able to state their wishes before they enter into such a state, for having entered it they can no longer do so. They would have to record their wish that in these circumstances some kindly doctor, by any direct or indirect means that he likes to devise shall put an end to their lives before they become an intolerable burden to their relatives and friends, their nurses and the state.

We come now to my third question: Is some kind of legislation desirable? What objections have been raised against it? There are those in the medical profession—perhaps the majority —who very naturally and understandably may accept euthanasia in principle and yet may refuse to take the active steps to carry it out. With this point of view I have the utmost sympathy; I am sure that there are many cases in which I would find myself in exactly that position. It is one thing to withdraw the antibiotics or to increase the morphine, but it is a different thing to go to someone in cold blood and administer a lethal injection. There are, however, ways in which this could be done much less blatantly if the doctor were fortified by the knowledge that it was the patient's expressed wish that his end should be hastened under these circumstances. We must, in medicine above all things, stick to our ethical principles, but we should make sure that we are not leaning on an appeal to morals simply to get ourselves out of a difficult and unwelcome situation.

During the debate, of those who opposed legislation, a good many were clearly arguing with the case of terminal cancer in mind and telling us that legislation was unnecessary, and all would agree with Lord Amulree that medical students and doctors in their postgraduate training years should be given far more instruction in the terminal care of old age and chronic illness, but that this does not excuse us from taking action now, if action is needed. Other doctors said that patients do not ask for euthanasia and I am sure that this is largely true: a patient places himself in his doctor's hands, he looks to the doctor to relieve his suffering and his pain, and he does not ask for more. But this again is not the case I have in mind, it is the case where the patient paralysed in speech and limb is totally incapable of expressing an opinion.

Other objections seemed to me to have little substance, or to show a misunderstanding of the whole purpose of a voluntary euthanasia bill; some called it suicide by proxy as if that argued against it. Some objected to the idea that you should have to sign a document in advance as to your wishes; it was, they said, like joining a club. It is a club which I would gladly join to-morrow; I might even put a badge on my car in case of a motor accident. The whole point of the bill is that you should be able to declare your wishes while you are still capable of expressing them.

Baroness Serota quoted Lord Horder from a previous debate as having said that the incurable today is the curable tomorrow; this I find to be rather a naïve statement. I remember a man who in 1923 or 1924 was in the last stages of diabetes; insulin came just in time and he lived until 1968. This is the kind of thing that Horder meant. But surely none of us thinks that a patient who has been immobile and speechless from a stroke for six months and whose brain is largely destroyed, is going to find himself cured by some wonder drug or by transplant surgery within the foreseeable, or at any rate his foreseeable, future.

To me the serious objections to legislation are threefold, but I am not sure that they cannot all be overcome by a redrafted bill together with a new consideration by the medical profession. The first is the natural objection of a doctor to the taking of life. The second which was raised in the debate was that certain hospitals, or certain nursing homes, where old and incurable patients were admitted would get the reputation of being places where you were 'bumped off' whether you wanted it or no; such a reputation might be quite unjustified but rumours spread rapidly. The third objection is that every old person though quietly and happily enjoying the evening of life, might feel that it was his duty to his relatives to sign a declaration that he wanted euthanasia; but in the bill as proposed by Lord Raglan this kind of person would not be a patient qualified for euthanasia, at any rate until he had reached a stage of incurable illness when he would no longer be able to signify his wishes.

It seems clear to me that unless you have dogmatic Catholic views, euthanasia is not a subject to be brushed aside, but that further discussion amongst intelligent and informed people must continue and public opinion must be sounded from time to time. Those most interested in the subject should study all the objections to legislation and see whether they could be overcome.

Not long ago the Earl of Listowel showed me a form which the Voluntary Euthanasia Society has issued. It has no legal significance but it indicates the wishes of anyone who, like myself, is in good health but dreads being kept mischievously alive in a vegetative state. It may at least serve to relieve the conscience of a medical attendant who is in doubt as to what course of action he can take. I have myself signed two copies of the form and had them witnessed, left one with my doctor and the other amongst instructions to those who may have to look after me.

15. Abortion

The Offences against the Person Act of 1861 states that 'any woman who, with intent to procure a miscarriage, administers to herself any poison or drug or uses any instrument for like purpose' is guilty of an offence and is liable to imprisonment for life, and so is any other person who administers drugs or uses any instrument on a woman for the same purpose. This, believe it or not, was in force until 1967, when the new Abortion Bill passed into law after long, and at times heated, discussion in both Houses of Parliament. In recent years, however, the law had not been enforced in its harshest terms, and in several cases in which medical men had been involved, the judges in their directions to juries had interpreted the law so as to absolve a doctor from penalty if he honestly believed that a mother's life or health was in serious danger.

Clearly, then, the law needed reform, if only to bring it into line with what had become current legal practice, and those who wanted the law reformed mostly wanted to go somewhat further and make the law less restrictive than it had previously been. In other words to make it easier for a woman who wanted an abortion to have it done legally and properly by a qualified doctor in proper premises, for everyone knew that enormous numbers of illegal abortions were being carried out, sometimes with disastrous effects on the subsequent health of the mother, and sometimes for exorbitant fees. But how many illegal abortions were taking place, and how much easier legal abortion should be made, and how much it would lessen the number of illegal abortions no one knew, for the mere fact of liberalizing the abortion law might, or would, in the opinion of some, increase the numbers of unwanted pregnancies. These were certainly important areas for debate.

Abortion is always undesirable; a bad answer to an unfortunate or in some cases intolerable situation. The right answer to unwanted pregnancy is prevention and education, that is, contraception; the right answer to poverty and overcrowding is social rather than medical, as Baroness Emmet of Amberley rightly said, but as I pointed out, her words would have had more weight if she could tell us how the housing situation and other social evils could be put right overnight. No one, least of all the afflicted mother, wants to resort to abortion, which involves the destruction of human life, and I can well understand that no doctor enjoys doing it.

Throughout the debate there was a tendency to lose sight of some of the facts. However undesirable abortion may be there are tens of thousands of women every year in this country who seek it as an escape from their situation. A law or an organized group of doctors which shuts its eyes to that fact is providing no answer. The argument that there are not the hospital beds available, which we have heard many times from some of the most authoritative of medical spokesmen, is sheer hypocrisy, for if we know one thing about abortion it is that a very large number of women will see that they get it, if not in hospital then elsewhere. The very people who say there are not enough beds or trained personnel are crying out for more deliveries to take place in hospital rather than at home for safety reasons. Every prompt and efficient abortion, let them be reminded, prevents a delivery later on or illness from an illegal abortion, either of which will be much more demanding of bed-occupation and manpower. (This answer is not of course absolute; if women went on having abortions every few months they might need more beds, but although such cases can be quoted they are admitted to be rare.)

Now as to the moral and ethical arguments. Whatever we may think of pre-marital intercourse (which seems now to be the rule rather than the exception) most people view promiscuity with disapproval, and anything which encourages it is therefore to be avoided. But the prevention of promiscuity is at a different level, the argument that freer abortion laws encourage it was not very seriously pursued, though perhaps it could have been.

Then there were arguments about the sanctity of human life, which is a difficult subject. When does a foetus become an individual or develop a soul as some of the theologians would put it? We cannot look to nature for an answer, for in biology there are no dividing lines. Presumably an ovum or a sperm is a living thing, but nature destroys them by the million in order that some few shall have a chance of survival. 'Nature' (one must never say 'God' when being critical) seems to have no ethical code. Animals kill and eat one another; the laws of genetics are the laws of chance. Man must make his own codes. Anything which implies a lesser regard for human life, which is what abortion to some extent is bound to do, must be treated with great caution. But is it a disregard or a regard for the quality of human life which makes many of us favour a more liberal approach to abortion?

Great talk there was over the clause permitting abortion if there was a substantial chance of the baby being mentally or physically handicapped. Here again there was some nonsense put forward about the three normal foetuses destroyed because one might be handicapped (according to the odds of the genetic stakes). This is a false argument when applied to cases where a handicapped child may result from a pregnancy complicated by german measles, for instance. For most of these pregnancies will be wanted ones, and the mother can shortly become pregnant again.

I get rather tired of arguments by old men about what should happen to young women, especially when ethics and principles are brought in, and it was to me a relief to hear Lord Soper, clergyman and social worker, who has really seen distress as it exists. In his words*

...Nobody has the right to be born. I am concerned about the right of those who are born, to live. I am concerned about their right to happiness; and it is the enormous weight of suffering that is now undergone by all kinds of humans in all

* From the second-reading debate on abortion. Hansard H/L 10.5.67.

kinds of circumstances connected with pregnancy that afflicts me. I speak with great care. I remember the Irish mother who, having listened for some time to a young celibate priest who was instructing her in the duties of motherhood, said: 'I wish to God I knew as little about it as he does.' This, I think, is not an inappropriate comment. Only one member of the opposite sex has taken part in this debate....

I could take your Lordships tonight to a little girl of 16 in a hostel which I run who is pregnant as the result of a drunken brawl and who is now almost out of her mind.... If that pregnancy is allowed to come to term it will leave her with a permanent trauma and an imperishable memory. She hates everything associated with pregnancy; she is frightened to death. I cannot for the life of me see why this kind of suffering should be imposed on her if she could be relieved of it. I could take you, if I were permitted, to a woman and seven children in an overcrowded tenement....

I believe that this bill is substantially right in attempting to reduce the amount of misery that is now undergone by— I do not know how many women.... If there is no final and irrevocable moral objection to preserving the foetal life at the expense of the welfare—the well-being, as the Church Assembly has said—of the mother and of her total environment, then there is in my judgment an overwhelming case for the presentation of such a bill as this.

In the second place I am oppressed by the sense of social injustice. I know a little about the facility with which it is possible for those who have money to obtain abortions, and to obtain them secretly. I know something of the back-street abortions, the iniquity of them and—what has not been mentioned this afternoon—the blackmail associated with them. The intolerable racket and the sleazy, dreadful conditions under which these abortions are carried out add to the misery.

...It seems to me that we are in great danger of asserting a sacrosanct nature for the foetal life at the very moment when the same Church is committing millions of human beings of adult stature to mutual massacre in mass violence and war. There seems to be much hypocrisy in this over-assiduity with which we are concerning ourselves with the choice of life of the future human being. Until we are prepared to take a like concern for the adult and fairly full life of those who have grown to self-conscious maturity, we shall not, I think, attract much attention from those who see this as a great evil and are not particularly concerned with the pseudo-scientific and, as I think, pseudo-theological reasons that we advance.

The present state of medical research strongly suggests that a simple 'do-it-yourself' method of abortion may soon be possible. In discussions on this subject I clearly detect, amongst some of those whose moral principles were all against abortion reform, a slight slackening of the intensely righteous attitude previously held. Could it be that the medical profession is prepared to provide the wherewithal for others to perform an immoral act which they themselves would not approve?

16. Music

My father wrote a small book on child-music, largely derived from the musical inventions of my brother and myself. Small children aged two or even less will invent tunes spontaneously, usually songs to their own words like 'Oh the sun is on the bath, the sun is on the bath' (words and music by my brother Maurice). Father (who gave illustrations) made out that my brother and I, aged four and two respectively, would occasionally sing in canon. Quite small children can recognize and repeat tunes with accuracy, though their voices are often a little off pitch; that is, their intervals may be slightly faulty, like a violinist whose intonation is imperfect. This, I should guess is due to insufficient technical skill in the use of the larynx rather than to faulty aural appreciation.

At a very early age, probably about four, I used to go with my brother Maurice to a class in Tonic Sol-fa run by an extraordinary personality called Miss Mills, at the house of Mrs Walter Russell Rea (as she then was), mother of the present Lord Rea, she having been at college with my mother.

To this day Maurice, Lord Rea and I are the only people I know who can translate music immediately into Sol-fa, and we think of music in this way. To say that we can sing everything in Sol-fa would be an exaggeration now that we have to contend with modern music of the atonal kind which is not really in any key at all, because Sol-fa then becomes meaningless. But in ordinary music one always knows the key note however often it changes and every note has its name in the chromatic scale in relation to the keynote. Academic descriptions such as the subdominant or supertonic or the leading note we treat with contempt, we just call them Fa, Ray and Te, and we know at once when the key changes, because, for instance, in a change from G major to C minor, what was Doh has suddenly become Me. Some of Schubert's enharmonic changes or the slow movement of Debussy's String Quartet gain in fascination and musical appreciation when every note has a name which you can give it at once without thought, but all this is difficult to explain to anyone who does not experience it, and unnecessary to explain to anyone who does. I think an early Sol-fa training makes the understanding of musical key, interval and harmonic change much more vivid, but it probably holds you back from learning staff-notation which may be one reason why I am to this day a bad sight-reader.

As a child of less than five (for we were still in Hampstead) I spent much time exploring and improvising on the piano and could play any simple tune such as 'God Save the King' with a simple but appropriate bass-part, and I discovered for myself methods of modulating from key to key, from C major through G, D, A, E etc., down again through the flat keys to B flat and F and so finally back to C major.

Such early musical experiment has advantages, for it is always better for the understanding to discover things for yourself, but its very freedom can militate against the acquisition of technique in the early years when technique could most easily be learned.

The innovation, as it was in my early days, of recorded music and later the radio, has given everyone opportunities of hearing good music well played which were non-existent in my childhood, but the consequent dearth of pianos, which could formerly be found in every middle-class home, became a serious disadvantage to another side of musical education. In quite recent years the tremendous growth of music teaching in schools is making up for this, and is also shifting the emphasis away from the keyboard (because there is no piano at home on which to practise) towards stringed and wind instruments which are portable.

Amongst the more well-to-do, the 'English Public School Tradition' of the nineteenth and early twentieth centuries, with its emphasis on Classics, Leadership and Rugby football, had a bad influence on musical education. Musicians were cissies, or hired entertainers, and more shocking still, very often foreigners, so that you had to do unBritish things like mixing with Germans, Czechs, Poles and other undesirables in order to get a string quartet together; or music was for young ladies singing ballads at the piano.

Of course those who could afford the time and the money went to concerts, and even for those who were hard up, there were very cheap seats, but there was little incentive to play music in the home or to learn any instrument except the piano.

This public school embargo on playing music may be the reason why nineteenth-century Britain produced no Schubert, no Brahms, no Debussy, Chopin, Mendelssohn or Tchaikowsky.

I should of course not forget that organists were respectable, I suppose because of their close connexion with the Church which was so much bound up with the origins of the public schools and older universities, but as a musician friend of mine once remarked: organists are a class apart. They talk like Bishops: 'I wonder who'll get Gloucester' and that kind of thing.

For one short period of my life I thought I might be wrong about the influence of the public schools. It lasted for about a quarter of an hour: I was dining at the Athenaeum one night and was talking to Wilson Smith, the virologist who, like me, was never at an English public school. He had a beautiful Guadagnini violin; I had played quartets with him and we discussed chamber music. Suddenly an old gentleman on my left, whom I knew by sight to be the elder brother of a very eminent statesman, asked if we had played the Mozart and Brahms clarinet quintets and if I had played the Brahms Opus 114 Trio for Piano, Clarinet and Cello. 'Isn't it Opus 115?' said I. 'No,' he replied, 'Opus 115 is the quintet.' (He was right.) I was amazed for I felt sure that a man from such an illustrious family must have been educated at Eton and Oxford or similar places. He told us that he had played the clarinet for many years, but like most of his generation found some modern music rather baffling. He said he had once been in an orchestra and

on turning the page suddenly noticed that his part was headed
'Clarinet in A' and he was playing it on his B flat clarinet. 'But
no one noticed in that kind of music,' he said. I was still
amazed, for we were talking in a language unknown to the
typical products of Britain's Great Public Schools. Then suddenly he added, without prompting, as if realizing he had
rather let the side down: 'You see when I was a boy I had a
long illness and never went to public school.'

At seven I had regular piano lessons, not I think very good
ones, and by this time I could so quickly pick up tunes and
pieces by ear and by memory, that sight-reading of anything
I was at all capable of playing was virtually unnecessary. This
also has led to later difficulties and regrets. I envy good sight-
readers who must have great fun, though I sometimes think
they are in danger of lacking depth in musical interpretation.
Great soloists are not always either good sight-readers or good
ensemble players. My piano teacher at this time was a Frenchwoman who had the usual foreigner's difficulty with the
English 'th'. One day she said to me 'play it wid de tum' which
put me into lots of giggles, for at that age any mention of the
tummy, being slightly indelicate, was therefore frightfully
funny.

At nine, my father invited to our house in Hendon the
Belgian violinist, Desiré Defauw (then I suppose a youth of
twenty-four) and a French 'cellist called La Grillière. They played
their instruments and my father then asked me which I would
like to learn. Without hesitation I said the 'cello, though to this
day I would find it difficult to explain why. I do not remember
my brother being offered a similar choice but I think this was
part of a plan, as he, nearly two years older, was already
making good progress on the piano.

My first experience of chamber music was hearing the
Brodsky Quartet playing in Sheffield about 1911, and noting the
tears on old Brodsky's cheek as they ended the slow movement
of Beethoven's Opus 132. Soon after this, when I was having

lessons in Sheffield from Colin Smith, a wealthy patron gave him £300 (a lot of money in those days) to buy a really good 'cello. He acquired a Ruggieri (which I suppose would now be worth a few thousand pounds) and made me sit in another room while he played the Ruggieri and his former instrument in turn. I had to guess which he played first. I felt almost sick at the awful possibility of giving the wrong answer, but in the event I found no difficulty.

Much later we had experiences with our own children. My son was composing quite passable music at the age of fourteen, and taking up the piano accordion (in which chords are given to you ready-made to choose from) probably helped a good deal in his early education in harmony.

Our third child (Helen) went to her first concert a few weeks before she was born, and her movements became so active and apparently joyful that her mother nearly had to leave the concert hall. Later on this child was devoted to her collection of gramophone records which she would play on her portable record player for hours at a time.

We did three experiments with Helen (who later took a degree in Music). We would mix up her records long before she could read, and say 'play me so and so'. She would at once find it, even though many of the records had the same kind of label. If it was not the right way up for the side she was asked to play she would turn it over, and then wind up the gramophone.

One Christmas about that time I gave her a few records (they were not so expensive then as long-playing records are today). Some were serious music, though not too difficult—Delius's Serenade from *Hassan* was one of those I remember—and some were popular music (Charlie Kunz at the piano was her favourite at that time). By subtle and discreet questioning I tried to ascertain whether she distinguished between these two kinds of music in any way, whether in other words she recognized not only that they were playing different tunes, but that they were different *kinds* of music. At that age no such distinction seemed to occur to her. She liked them equally well, and played them with equal enjoyment.

When the D'Oyley Carte Opera Company came to Sheffield I booked seats (in the front row of the dress circle) for *The Gondoliers*, this being, I thought, less frightening for a small child than, say, *The Mikado*. I also borrowed the records of the whole opera and for a fortnight or so before the performance we would play excerpts from it, without comment of any kind, at meal-times, playtimes or bedtime. We then took Helen to the Opera. Of course by that time she knew all the music and every time the orchestra introduced a new song she at once recognized it and had to be dissuaded, with difficulty, from standing up and *conducting* the music from the dress circle. Moreover, although she must have been no more than four years old, she retained her interest throughout the performance and was quite cross when it ended.

Absolute pitch, sometimes erroneously called perfect pitch, is a phenomenon which interests me biologically, genetically and musically. There is so much misunderstanding about it that it is even difficult to have an unemotional discussion on the subject. Those who have it tend to pride themselves upon the fact, and cannot see how people can be really musical or musicians without it. Those who, like the majority, do not have absolute pitch, point out that it has little or no relationship to being musical at all. What really matters to the musician is relative pitch, and many noted composers and musicians, including Schubert and Wagner (both writers of superb melody), were without absolute pitch.

Absolute pitch is absolute in another respect. Either you have it or you do not. As Dr Van der Pol once said (See Grove's *Dictionary of Music* under 'Pitch, absolute') 'no one who really possesses absolute pitch can be in any doubt about it'.

The faculty of absolute pitch, if present, can be revealed in two ways. Strike a note on the piano without warning and I will not have the slightest idea what note it is (though of course I would know whereabouts it was and might with luck guess it within a tone or two) but do the same to my friend Sylvia, who has absolute pitch, and she will say at once, correctly, 'E flat' (or whatever) and moreover she will say it without any recognizable mental process intervening. Once having established that a certain note is E flat, you can then play any other note, and I shall be as good as anyone in naming the second note, but not without going through a moment of deliberation in which I am consciously *relating* the second note to the first. Hence the term relative pitch. For instance if the second note is a major third above the E flat, obviously it must be G. This deliberate moment of calculation seems to be unnecessary to those who have absolute pitch. Conversely, say to Sylvia (without previous warning) 'sing D flat' and she will accurately do so, whereas I could only do it in relation to a note already sung or played.

It must be satisfying, and in some respects very useful, to have absolute pitch, but the person with relative pitch is in no way prevented from being just as good a musician, who can judge his intervals, and play his violin, with perfect accuracy. Should he however, hear the National Anthem, for instance, played on the piano, he would not know whether it was being played in its usual key of G, or whether the pianist had transposed it to F sharp just for fun, unless he had been given a note of reference.

There is in fact one way in which the person with absolute pitch is at a disadvantage; if I were to play 'God save the Queen' on a piano which had been tuned a semitone below the usual concert pitch, I should be unaware of it, but a person with absolute pitch might be badly put off and confused by the fact that the notes heard were not the same as the notes written!

When we come to consider the subject biologically we must remember that within the inner ear is a remarkable membrane about one-8,oooth of an inch in thickness and one and a quarter inch in length, with about 24,000 fibres embedded in it, ranging in length from one-15th to a 170th of an inch.* The short fibres

* I quote from Sir James Jeans, *Science and Music*, Cambridge University Press, 1937.

which are analogous to the treble wires of the piano are very tightly stretched, the ones at the other end—the bass wires— are much looser. The fibres are set in motion according to the shape, pattern and rhythm of the sound waves reaching them, so that one must assume that ordinary people can discern and appreciate musical sounds by knowing the intervals between the fibres which are vibrating, whereas persons with absolute pitch can actually, by some mysterious process, tell just which fibres are vibrating.

The whole subject is made more difficult by the fact that people with absolute pitch cannot actually name those vibrating fibres until they have been in some way musically educated. A small child may have the faculty of absolute pitch built in, but you cannot say 'sing E flat' because he has not yet learnt which of the sounds he identifies is called E flat. Thus, although the faculty is almost certainly inherited and inborn, it seems well nigh impossible to test for it and detect its presence in early infancy.

This, and general ignorance of the subject, makes it very difficult to determine the mechanism of the heredity of absolute pitch. It appears, by hearsay, to be a Mendelian dominant, in that in musical families you are often told by someone with absolute pitch 'My mother (or father) had it and I think my eldest daughter has, but I know my brother (or sister) hasn't.' But very rarely can you go back another generation because the deceased relatives may never have been tested or musically educated.

Finally the subject is further obscured by people who from long practice of tuning a stringed instrument have acquired a fairly accurate sense of pitch in that they can take up an un- tuned instrument and say 'I think the A is a little sharp (or flat)' and they will often be right. But this is the product of long experience; like being able to judge the time without a watch, it does not rely on some built-in mechanism which other people lack.

* * *

Of all recreations music must be one of the best, for it can carry you away within minutes from whatever other world you normally live in, especially if you play it—or even practise it—yourself. Any subject which has an intellectual and creative content becomes more and more rewarding as you get to know more about it (provided you have not been taught it at a university) and if it is a practical art, the more you become practised at it. So must it be for painting, but I could never paint or draw, although my elder daughter can (or could until she went to the Slade School, after which she gave it up for several years).

Music is a communication of a unique kind, which is independent of speech although it is itself a kind of language with an undoubted logic, as all who know the Forty-eight Preludes and Fugues or the Brandenburg Concertos must concede. 'The celestial logic of Bach', Russell Brain once called it. It is a language in which we recognize the gay and the light-hearted, or the sad, the superficial and the profound; the lovely sentimental 'wallowing' music, as I call it, of *La Bohème* or the Mendelssohn Violin Concerto, or the profound soul-searching music of the late Beethoven quartets, or the superb and distinguished music of that great innovator, Debussy. Then there is programme music, good and bad, of which Tchaikowsky's *Romeo and Juliet* overture is a good example.

Some snobs profess to look down on programme music but Richard Strauss refused to recognize the distinction between abstract and programme music. For him there was only good music and bad, and good music was that which expressed most. Degrees of good and bad can easily be discerned in pop music old and modern. There is certain genius in 'Night and Day', and the ground bass of 'Day Tripper' (the Beatles) would have been a joy to Monteverdi; while the taking over by the drums in 'In a gadda da vida' (played by Iron Butterfly) is to me very reminiscent of the famous takeover bid of the harpsichord in the Fifth Brandenburg Concerto.

Finally there is 'cliché' music, heard in every American hotel and now in many restaurants in Britain, from which there is no escape except to pay more to do without it. And the greatest sin of all in music is to take a melody from some superb work of a great master and rewrite it as a popular tune. Chopin's *Fantaisie-Impromptu* was murdered in this way. Cliché music once heard runs round and round in the head. Very early in life I discovered, as hundreds of others must have done, that to get rid of it you must mentally replace it by some other less head-running and less irritating music. When I was very young I used to find 'Rule Britannia' a good antidote but there are plenty of better choices.

Music, unlike pictorial art, is temporal, and so it can use the devices of repetition, variation, and above all, suspense. Witness the long harpsichord solo in the Fifth Brandenburg Concerto where one is almost bursting in suspense at the continual postponement of the expected return of the orchestra. Witness Sibelius's 'run up to the wicket' towards the end of the last movement of his Second Symphony where the strings, and later some of the wind, play a rapid repetitive passage in D minor for seventy-three bars only to lead up to the climax in D major in the seventy-fourth. Or take the suspense in that wonderful slow movement of Beethoven's A minor quartet Opus 132 which keeps coming, one thinks, to a beautiful and quiet close only to lead on to some even more beautiful afterthoughts. Or Wagner's gradual development of the 'Prize Song' in *The Mastersingers*; or the almost unbearable titillation in Tchaikowsky's *Romeo and Juliet* overture, of the music leading up to the love theme, which finally breaks through with unbelievable beauty exactly a semitone lower than you had been prepared for.

Music is not ashamed of its emotional appeal, which pure scientific argument, narrow and limited as it is, professes to eschew, but, as in true love-making, the appeal must be aesthetic and not vulgar.

Music crosses all boundaries of nationality, language, politics, age, sex and education. If you play music with others, as in a string quartet, you live in a different world where it is good to dwell and you achieve a sense of oneness with the other members of the quartet which gradually dissolves again as the music ends and your individuality returns.

Music makes clear that man has a soul or a spirit, call it what you will, which needs aesthetic satisfaction, and this no doubt he shares with other musical animals such as the thrush, the lark and the nightingale.

This century has seen great progress in man's control of his environment but it is questionable whether this has been accompanied by any equivalent gain in the Arts. Some would say just the reverse. I know from experience how difficult and dangerous it is to judge contemporary art and music and I remember my father telling me of the heated controversies in his time on whether the 'awful stuff' produced so prolifically by Richard Wagner could be called music at all. Yet I cannot believe that throwing nails, paint and match-boxes on to a piece of canvas will ever be considered as a serious contribution to art, nor will I believe that music which consists of a concatination of random sounds without pattern, design or emotional expression will ever claim the serious attention of future generations. There must surely be some effort, some inspiration, some pangs in any creative process worthy of the name.

W. M. S. Russell has put together some interesting facts on the process of creation* which is very similar in art and in science. First comes the period of preparation much of it spent in observation and reflexion—at times relaxed and enjoyable, at other times demanding painfully hard work—and the conquest of inertia. Tchaikowsky said that one should not wait too long for the coming of the inspired mood. It must be met halfway. Then there may be a stage of incubation followed, often quite suddenly, by the inspiration which may seem to come from outside and to be accompanied by a sense of certainty and belief in its rightness.

'I am making some slight changes to the text, but who am I to tamper with a masterpiece?' Oscar Wilde remarked when a friend found him working at one of his manuscripts. In the final stage the full technical mastery is required to translate

* 'Art, Science and Man', *The Listener* 9.1.64, p. 43.

the inspiration into something which can be communicated. To some this is easy, to others the most difficult stage of all. I cannot believe that so-called modern art or music of the kind which seems to require none of these efforts has any greatness.

This of course is not a sweeping condemnation of all that is modern in art or music. Beethoven was modern in his day but conscious of his own greatness, and unconcerned that his audiences found his late quartets difficult to understand, for he knew that some day they would be accepted. When one of his musicians (probably Schuppanzigh) pointed to difficulties in the execution of the music, Beethoven said 'Glaubt er, dass ich an seine elende Geige denke, wenn der Geist über mich kommt?' (Does he imagine I'm thinking of his wretched fiddle when the inspiration comes over me?) To him the musicians and their instruments were the servants, not the masters, of the music, but his technical craftsmanship in the creation of his quartets, as well as their inspiration, was superb.

It is remarkable how human skills (like running the four-minute mile) continue to develop and improve as new techniques are learnt. When Tchaikowsky had written his violin concerto for Leopold Auer, one of the great violinists of his day, the latter pronounced it unplayable. Now it is in the repertory of every player of concerto standard. Mischa Elman made his début with this work at the Queen's Hall in London in 1906. The late Sir Henry Dale (one-time president of the Royal Society) told me how he and his brother Benjamin Dale, the composer, were present at the performance. In the interval they met Cunningham Woods, a music critic of the time. He told the Dales that he had been sitting next to a very old gentleman who, obviously much moved by Elman's playing, put a tremulous hand on his shoulder saying 'I do not know who you are, sir, but I must tell you that this is the finest playing I have heard since Paganini.' As this was 1906 and Paganini died in 1840 the statement came as something of a surprise, but it turned out that the old man was Manuel Garcia, the famous teacher of singing who was born in 1805 and was then 101 years old. He would have been thirty-five when Paganini died, and had no doubt heard him many times.

Manuel Garcia invented the laryngoscope to look at the vocal cords of his students; an instrument still used daily by doctors.

17. Reflections on Religious Belief

My father and mother, who were respectively thirty-three and thirty-seven when I was born, were amongst the advanced and radical set of their day, influenced by the artistic, literary and musical pioneers of those times, many of whom they knew personally; and I cannot remember any serious reference to religion during the time that we lived in Hampstead and Hendon, that is until I was ten years old. We never went to church, we never read the Bible or the prayer book, and anything we knew about God or Jesus Christ must have been learnt at school, though at King Alfred's school in Hampstead at that time it would have been mighty little.

Yet my mother had received a firm religious upbringing since her mother was a pillar of the Episcopal Church in Scotland. Every year we went to Tayport in the summer holidays, and the only religious instruction I ever remember my parents giving me was some hasty pre-Scotland instruction on how to find my place in the prayer book, the avowed purpose of which was simply to ensure that granny should not suspect that my brother and I had not attended church since the year before. I do remember having a twinge of conscience over this, or perhaps of surprise, that my parents, until then supposedly perfect in their moral behaviour, were practising this deception; I argued that as its purpose was to avoid hurting granny's feelings, it was excusable.

When we moved to Grindleford in 1910 to start the school my parents thought that some kind of concession to orthodoxy had to be made. Father would give occasional talks based on the Bible and those who wished went to church on Sunday mornings. As music was already deeply rooted within me I used to sing in the choir or pump the organ (by hand in those days) for the organist. For a brief period of my life I felt that I ought to embrace the Faith and become a member of the Church. As I had never been baptized this meant going through the ceremony of later baptism before confirmation. This I did. My parents were against infant baptism for they felt that children should decide for themselves later in life. (My brother always held that you should be baptized but not confirmed, the responsibility for your sins then remained indefinitely with your godparents!)

My interest in the Church was, however, of short duration, and although these are memories of long ago I feel certain that my break with the Church, no doubt inevitable sooner or later because of my temperament and upbringing, was at least hastened by an emotional conflict; my religious coaching prior to confirmation soon made it clear to me that there were important elements in my current friendship with one Dora which would not have claimed the full approval of the Church. Dora won, for like the young Dr Burney 'I always had an ardent passion for her person', but I do not think she played a deliberate part in my renunciation of religion. I should think that like most people of those days and even today who had a conventional upbringing she probably regarded the Church as a kind of ritual which you accepted but did not allow to influence your private life and feelings. But for me it had to be one thing or the other, and I have never had cause to regret my decision.

I have often made it plain in my spoken and written words that I do not believe in an after-life or in any way subscribe to orthodox religious belief, and this has led to my being asked if I am an Agnostic or an Atheist. In common speech, or as a kind of shorthand, I am quite willing to be called either, but I do not think the question can be seriously asked without defining more clearly what it means. Agnosticism is not necessarily about God at all. It refers to the philosophical view that nothing is knowable except material phenomena. This to me is nonsense and would preclude any rational or interesting conversation. In any ordinary or meaningful sense I know all kinds of things; I know all kinds of non-material ways in which one person differs from another, for instance, and I can often predict how they will react to a situation or an idea. But use the word 'agnostic' in relation to God if you like, and let us see where it leads—and let us at the same time see if I am an Atheist.

If you care to define God, perhaps I can answer your questions. I cannot assert that there is no god for I do not know there is not. What I do assert is that if there is, he cannot be omniscient, omnipotent and benign all at the same time, for this leads us straight to illogicalities. If he is omniscient he knows, for instance, that the laws of genetics are the laws of chance. If omnipotent, they are of his own making and he alone could alter them. If benign, he would do so pretty quickly, for even if physical and mental suffering is part of some mysterious divine plan to do us all good in the long run, a benign deity would surely not dole it out by the toss of a coin or the throw of the dice.

The most heart-rending of all the well-known hereditary diseases is the type of muscular dystrophy which affects half the male children of an afflicted parentage. The plan behind it is about as diabolical as could be devised. The parents are not themselves affected, and may not know of near-relatives with the disease, and so have no warning beforehand that they should not have children. The disease does not develop at birth, but at about six to ten years old, when the child is growing up and so is well aware of what begins to happen to him. By this time, the parents, unwarned because of the late appearance of the disease, have perhaps two more sons whom they will now watch for signs of the developing disease. These boys in turn will watch their elder brother's muscular weakness slowly progress until he can no longer breathe and dies at the age of perhaps seventeen. They will, if they are affected, soon realize that they have the same relentless disease progressing to the same termination. Whether this realization is more distressing to the children or their parents is hard to say.

I could of course give hundreds of other examples of disease in children and in adults which are impossible for me, by any kind of mental gymnastics or appeals to Faith, to reconcile with a belief in a benign deity. I cannot accept that 'Man is the object of God's Love, as God has shown by His acts'* for my experience just does not bear it out. If we are to reject both reason and experience when talking of these things, what powers have we left to discuss the subject at all?

So if you ask me, do I believe in God, I answer I do not know. The superb structure and perfect functioning of my old humble friend the kidney makes me sometimes doubt whether Darwinian evolution is a sufficient explanation. So there may be a plan, and therefore a planner. If so, he has presumably planned the whole animal kingdom, the tiger's claw, the rules of animal life—kill and eat. Eat, anyway, dead or alive. I do not find that this helps me to recognize a god whom I could worship.

None of this denies that as human beings we have in us powers for good and evil and an appreciation of right and wrong, and that we have perhaps the greatest faculty of all, the appreciation of beauty (which presumably we share with many other animals). None of this precludes me from practising and teaching the ethics of medicine, and finally I must assert in the clearest of terms that the Humanist and Scientist, the Agnostic, the Atheist, are not people deprived of feeling. Indeed they may, as I know only too well, be most uncomfortably endowed with a talent for sharing some of the grief of those who suffer the slings and arrows of outrageous fortune.

It always strikes me that a common insecurity of religious belief is shown in the habit of always thanking *God* when something beneficial has occurred, such as a narrow escape from death, while blaming *Nature* for droughts, famines, epidemics and earthquakes. *The Times* (27.9.70) recently told us:

* Geoffrey Fisher, 'The doctor's creed', *The Lancet* 29.10.49, p. 775.

Earlier this summer millions of Indian families were praying for rain as they watched their meagre crops wither away on parched land. But nature has always been cruel to India and so when their prayers were answered the rains came with a vengeance.

A torrential downpour broke the banks of the mighty Indian rivers in six states to wipe away land, crops, entire families and villages in both the eastern and western provinces.

Of course this was India and the people may well have been praying to the wrong god, but the antithesis between God and nature was never more closely made.

No one says 'thank nature'. No one speaks of 'God's divine inspiration' in terms of being red in tooth and claw. We read of people in earthquakes whose first instinct is to pray for deliverance and whose second is to thank God when they are delivered. We hear of no one cursing God for killing the other 100,000 who came off less luckily. These absurdities are so elementary that one feels apologetic in pointing them out to presumably intelligent people.

One of my few excursions into print on religion was on the publication of the New English Bible. In a letter to *The Times* (19.3.70) I wrote:

Sir—The new translation of the Bible, going back as it does to original sources will be acclaimed as a work of immense and important scholarship.

Perhaps, now that it is written in a language all can understand, the Old Testament will be seen for what it is, an obscene chronicle of man's cruelty to man, selfishness and cupidity, backed up by his appeal to his god: a horror story if ever there was one.

It is to be hoped that it will at last be proscribed as totally inappropriate to the ethical instruction of schoolchildren.

This was followed by a number of letters pointing out that there were good passages as well as horrible ones in the Old Testament, pointing out its significance in the evolution of

161

religion and society (which I had acknowledged), picturing (for reasons which are obscure to me) God's attempts (rather futile it seems) to deal with the cruelty, cupidity and obscenities of mankind (was not mankind his creation?), showing (how, I don't understand) that Man without God is a destroyer.

A notable journal approached me to give them an article in which I could point out some of the passages which offended me but they refused to publish the article which I submitted. The passages I mentioned showed the general cruelty, bloodshed and violence in the Bible, such as Joshua (10:40) who 'massacred the population of the whole region—the hill-country, the Negeb, the Shephelah, the watersheds.... He left no survivor, destroying everything that drew breath, as the Lord the God of Israel had commanded.' Or the Book of Numbers (31:1-20), 'The Lord spoke to Moses ... 'You are to exact vengeance for Israel on the Midianites....' The armed men made war on Midian, slew all the men and took captive the women, carried off property and burned all the cities. But Moses spoke angrily to the officers 'Have you spared all the women? ... kill every woman who has had intercourse with a man, but spare for yourselves every woman among them who has not had intercourse....' (They took thirty-two thousand such girls of whom thirty-two seem to have been given to the priest as tax levied for the Lord.)

Even the murder of Sisera by Jael seems to have been approved by the Lord (Judges 4 & 5). You will remember that she drove a tent-peg into his skull while he was asleep. 'His brains oozed out on the ground, his limbs twitched, and he died.'

It is true that the Ten Commandments, which were no doubt an improvement on previous moral laws, derive from the Old Testament, but my theological friends who are keen to point this out forget about the awful penalties which the Lord exacts on the wrongdoers. If a woman given in marriage is found not to be a virgin 'they shall bring her out to the door of her father's house and the men of her town shall stone her to death' (Deuteronomy 22:21). If a man lies with a virgin who is already pledged to another, both shall be stoned to death (22:24). If a man commits adultery with his neighbour's wife, both shall be put to death. There is the same penalty for homosexual practices, and if a man takes both a woman and her mother both he and they shall be burnt (Leviticus 20).

If you would read of incest, try the story of Lot's daughters. The elder one made her father drunk and then lay with him, and persuaded her sister to do the same the next night. Both became pregnant and bore sons, thus keeping the family alive.

For further reading on sexual behaviour read how 'they set up a tent for Absalom on the roof, and he lay with his father's concubines in the sight of all Israel' (2 Samuel 16:22), or the story of David and Bathsheba (Chapter 11), how he saw her bathing, and she was beautiful, 'so he sent messengers to fetch her, and when she came to him, he had intercourse with her'. She became pregnant so he had her husband killed in battle.

But the worst story of all is in the Book of Judges (Chapter 19) where the wicked men of the town knock at the door of an old man and demand that he sends out his guest to them so that they can have intercourse with him. 'No, my friends,' says the old man, 'do nothing so wicked. This man is my guest; do not commit this outrage. Here is my daughter, a virgin; let me bring her out to you. Rape her and do to her what you please; but you shall not commit such an outrage against this man.' But the men were not satisfied so the guest took hold of his concubine and thrust her outside for them. They assaulted her and abused her and finally killed her, and her master cut up her body limb by limb into six pieces.

I gave some of these quotations to the House of Lords in the debate on pornography initiated by Lord Longford. I strongly recommend the Old Testament, especially in its New English version, to all who like to read of lust, horror, cruelty and violence, yet there are some who seem to think that it should be in every school library. It is sold in children's bookshops and I often wonder whether parents are ready and even eager for conversations of this kind: 'Mummy why did the man want them to rape his daughter? What is a concubine? Why did he cut her into six pieces, did God tell him to?' 'Hush, dear, you don't understand these things.' Probably the little dears are far too tactful to embarrass their parents in this way.

If anyone can convince me that God comes off well in all this, he, not God, will have performed a miracle. After my letter to *The Times* I had many private letters and personal good wishes from people who agreed with me and congratulated me on being outspoken. My brother wrote to me pointing out that Thackeray, in a letter to his mother dated 26 July 1845, wrote: 'I find there was a sect in the early Church who denounced the Old Testament: and get into such a rage myself when reading all that murder and crime wh. the name of the Almighty is blasphemously made to Sanction: that I don't dare trust myself to write, and put off my work from day to day.'*

As President of the Royal College of Physicians I had, of course, to make occasional concessions, such as attendance at memorial services. (I hope no one will hold one for me.) I also had to say grace before dinner. Realizing the three uses of the Latin subjunctive, I chose 'Sit Dei Nomen Sacrum in Saecula Saeculorum' (May the name of the Lord be praised for ever and ever) which could also mean 'The name of the Lord *may* (i.e. or may not) be praised' or 'The name of the Lord may (if you wish it) be praised', i.e. you have my permission to do so. This grace also has the advantage of not offending Jews and other denominations, and is to me a welcome change from 'For what we are about to receive ...' or 'Benedictus benedicat'.

Perhaps my final status in all this was summed up by Sir Theodore Fox, one-time editor of *The Lancet* whom I have known as a friend for many years. After he left *The Lancet* he became for some time Director of the Family Planning Association, and when he gave that up, I, being President of the F.P.A. wrote a very sincere though brief appreciation for *The Family Planning Journal*. Shortly afterwards I received a letter from him.

'Dear Robert, since leaving the F.P.A. I've spent most of my

---

* J. Y. T. Craig, *Thackeray—a reconsideration*, Oxford University Press, 1950.

time having 'flu; and I reckon I still have about ninety per cent disability from encephalitis, hepatitis and neurasthenia.

'But about half-way through the illness, I felt strong enough to look at *Family Planning*, and I must at least tell you that I think it extraordinarily good of you to have gone to the (considerable) trouble of writing those comforting words—perhaps, as a last resort, I'll show them to St Peter. "Robert Platt?" he'll say. "Not one of our lot"....'

18. Love and Biology

Speaking biologically sexual reproduction is a cunning genetic device for bringing variety, and therefore adaptability, into the next generation while ensuring at the same time, through natural selection, a certain stability derived from the fact that the outsize variants (whether in stature, intelligence, or social desirability) are less likely to find mates.

Along with the mating instinct, and closely allied to it is the nesting instinct which seeks to provide a home for the protection of the young. This is particularly important in the human race of which the young take so many years to mature; that is, to have equipped themselves by learning and physical development for existence independent of their parents (which prompts me to think that if the moralizers turned their attention now and then from pre-marital intercourse to the suppression of racketeers in housing and land values we might have a better society). This late maturation of the human young is favoured by a largely monogamous social behaviour pattern.

In sexual reproduction, as my readers are no doubt aware, the female has the job of protecting and supplying the needs of the child in the womb and in early infancy while the male goes off to hunt for food. Whether he does this by killing a buffalo or manipulating money (convertible into food and lodging) on the Stock Exchange depends on the degree of sophistication of the society in which he lives, but in either case he needs aggression while the female requires patience, most highly developed in birds who incubate their eggs.

There are of course differing degrees of these qualities; impatient and aggressive women are not unknown. Patient and submissive husbands also exist; wives often fulfil their ambitions through their husbands and can thus act as the driving force, even though not pursuing a profession of their own, and the female, as is well known, soon shows her fighting qualities if home and young are threatened, hence the intense nature of jealousy. The aggressive instinct of the male can be deviated into crime and we know that crime, especially violent crime including war, is, of all occupations, perhaps the one most nearly exclusive to the male. (The recent discovery that males who have two Y, i.e. male, chromosomes, instead of one, are usually in trouble with the police by the time they are fourteen is interesting here.)

These are some of the factors leading to the notion that in the search for a mate man is the seeker and woman the accepter. I say the notion, because of course the normal female, even before puberty, begins to practise the arts of self-adornment and sexual attractiveness. Nevertheless it is usually the male who makes the first overtures, or thinks he does, and by custom derived from all this, is the one who in most societies actually makes the proposal of marriage. Yet again, we must be careful not to be deceived. The acceptance is as important as the proposal, and the proposal will probably not be made if the attitude of the female is forbidding rather than inviting; it takes two to make a courtship—or a seduction.

The former Lord Chancellor (Lord Gardiner) recently told us in the House of Lords during the debate on the second reading of the Divorce Reform Bill, 'It is a simple fact that if you take the most common case, based on adultery alone, the number of petitions by wives against adulterous husbands is always just about the same as the number of petitions by husbands against adulterous wives.... I think that in 1966 there were more adulterous wives than husbands; in 1967 cases of adultery by wives numbered 11,061, by husbands 11,016 ... and last year, 1968, by wives 13,171; by husbands 12,800 ... there is a difference of a few hundreds each year, one way or the other.' (Hansard H/L 30.6.69.)

These facts, which seem to come as a surprise to many, are even more remarkable when we remember that many of the divorces were really a matter of collusion and that in such cases it was customary for the man somewhat chivalrously to agree to put himself in the wrong, socially speaking.

Nevertheless during the debate many noble Lords seemed to be unable to take in the facts of life and went on gallantly talking about abandoned wives as if abandoned husbands did not exist. Of course there is often an important financial difference between the two situations and the new laws were particularly concerned with seeing that this was looked after as far as possible. The new Act has now come into operation and figures for adulterous behaviour will be much more difficult to come by, so it is important to remember Lord Gardiner's statistics.

Nature, or should we say evolution, has made the sexual act and the seduction and courtship which precede it an intensely pleasurable and, at best, a magical experience. Men and women vary greatly in their talents and in the extent to which they cultivate the arts of love-making. I sometimes wish I had known Lady Elizabeth Foster, whose allurements, Gibbon said, could beckon the Lord Chancellor from his Woolsack.

Although the monogamous form of social behaviour has evolved because it is without doubt the best for the maturing offspring there must be few who could sincerely say that they could only feel the pleasures of sexual attraction once in a life-time or with only one partner. And so the problem is how to make a compromise between the ideals of monogamy and the instincts which lead into the seductive situation, and whether the ideals and the pattern of sexual behaviour are being, or will be, altered by the discovery of well-nigh perfect contra-ceptive techniques. The present contraceptive pill is not ideal. It is liable to alter, if only slightly, a woman's temperament and also her figure, as well as to upset her physiology, perhaps for many years. No one really knows yet what the long-term results will be. Neither is abortion an answer to any of the problems involved, although in some instances it may be the lesser of two bad alternatives.

Much is said at the present time and not without reason, of the sadly frequent unwanted pregnancies in young women and girls, especially in students (perhaps because our moralizers argue that they are intelligent and should know better). Some blame the women in accordance with age-old tradition. Some with more justice blame the irresponsible male who expects his female partner to look after herself.

Much more often, I believe, it is the result of a compelling urge between two people overwhelmed by the life force, which drives the man on and on towards fulfilment with an ever more willing partner, and at the climax nature is not satisfied until the magic fluid which creates the new life has been passed from the male into the female. And at this ultimate moment of ecstasy, whatever may have been the man's intentions of caution and last-minute evasion, it can be the woman, driven now by all the forces of nature and regardless of the consequences who refuses to let him go until the act of impregnation has been achieved. Once roused, a woman's compelling passion can be at least as strong as a man's.

Although for many reasons this is not a situation to be encouraged lightly and for social, emotional and biological reasons promiscuity is undesirable, as it stops short of the homing instinct which is the basis of a good marriage and a happy family, I nevertheless tire of sociologists, psychiatrists or moralizers if they talk as if this intense sexual drive is something which can be quite easily controlled and turned on and off like the heat of an electric fire.

However difficult it is to give any guidance to young people, they should at least know the facts. Not only the bald physiological facts and a catalogue of the advantages of different contraceptives, but the evolutionary, emotional and psycho-social facts, as far as they can usefully be presented. It is extraordinary that until quite recently there was no discussion of these subjects in the medical curriculum or in any kind of school or university education. How the young doctor was expected to guide others I do not know. My own early education in these matters was entirely extra-curricular.

I would not, of course, claim that my own attempts to rationalize on the subject of sexual behaviour are wholly satisfactory, partly because emotion is not easily amenable to rational thought and argument, but even more because what nature through centuries of evolution intends us to do to keep the race in existence and what a highly developed society demands, are sometimes at variance, if not actually incompatible. Trying to put my thoughts into some kind of order, and even at times to pass them on to medical students, I seem to arrive at the following tentative conclusions as a basis for discussion.

The present generation of young people is not, as I know from my own experience, the first to be intensely interested in sex, nor is it the first to cause anxiety in its elders. We must not become obsessed with the idea that a revolution in sexual behaviour is going on which will have awful consequences for the world. It must be about 450 years since John Skelton wrote in a poem called 'The Maner of the World Now a Dayes':

> So many maidens with child
> And wylfully begylde ...
> So many women blamed
> And righteously defaimed
> And so lytle ashamed,
> Sawe I never.

Nevertheless we are perhaps seeing the first generation who are growing up in a society which has reliable and convenient methods of contraception, and which has escaped, or is escaping from the domination of the Church, with its morbid preoccupation with chastity and its encouragement of largely homosexual and male-dominated societies. Whether this is seen as a matter for regret, or as a challenge to the reassessment of sexual morals will depend on whether you believe that moral codes are given to us by some supernatural power, or whether you think they have evolved in relation to need, for the improvement and survival of our society.

In an approach to reassessment we should remember that delinquency is common in children who come from unstable marriages and broken homes. The code of behaviour will thus be judged eventually by whether it tends to lead to lasting human relationships, and, whatever two people may decide about sexual intercourse, they have a duty not to bring into the world a child who has not the wholly desirable background of a home and two loving parents.

Sexual intercourse, being a profound emotional experience, should be preceded, as it is in the animal kingdom, by a period of courtship. Nevertheless first experiences of courtship do not necessarily lead to a lasting bond, and the early experiments of adolescents may be valuable as a trial period before setting out on the responsibilities of bringing up a family.

Contraception is a matter for consideration by both parties and should not be a responsibility thrust on women alone. Neither should contraception and sexual behaviour in a medical school be taught solely by gynaecologists as if it were something which only concerns women.

For myself my earliest recollection of the dawnings of courtship was with Violet who I think was about eight years old when I was the same. We both went to King Alfred's school. I often used to take her home, sometimes catching a later train from Hampstead to Hendon in order to do so, and I suppose that she was the first to kindle within me the tender feelings of of boy–girl friendship. Certainly I could not have had similar feelings for a boy-friend. Nothing came of this of course; we just seemed to like each other's company. In spite of this early friendship, I really had very little curiosity about the other sex until I was in my teens; I recognized that girls were different from boys, and women from men, but did not show much initiative in finding out what those differences were, and as I had a brother but no sister I did not grow up with any obvious source of information.

I suppose that with the arrival of adolescence I became more interested, and it was then that I made a very intense friendship with a girl called Dora, who was older than I (perhaps seventeen when I was fifteen and a half), and very much more knowledge-able. She had had a strange experience in which a visitor to her house, much older than herself and on leave from the Merchant Navy, had enticed her into his bedroom where he proceeded to introduce her to the mysteries of sexual intercourse. She told me how she passed through a period of terror in which she remembered violently clutching her handkerchief. She was too frightened to resist or to scream, and then quite suddenly she discovered that the experience was intensely pleasurable. One wonders in retrospect whether her demeanour could have been entirely forbidding, or was there perhaps an element of startled curiosity?

Be that as it may, far from being deterred for life by this initial sexual experience, as some psychiatrists and others might have predicted, she took an intense interest in the subject and was one of the most important influences in my early education. This was carried out with a thoroughness and enthusiasm appropriate to such an important study.

Nevertheless it has been noted, and with truth, that adolescent boy–girl friendships, however serious at the time, are often transient, and I cannot in retrospect think that we were deeply in love, neither do I remember any feelings of bereavement when she became engaged to a young army officer. Yet there was certainly a time when I thought I should marry her and I think she was at least one of the factors in my choice of a career because, for some reason, she wanted to marry a doctor. Thus Dora may have influenced the whole of my future as well as unwittingly influencing my religious beliefs.

It would be nonsense to pretend that I could have lived my life without my women friends. Although some of these friendships have been intimate indeed, I think I have only been in love with three women in my life, and in saying that I am admitting to the recognition of Love as something which has a quality not achieved by mere friendship. Nor is it merely friendship accompanied by sexual excitement. And they loved me, desperately, passionately, irrationally.

Of course I was vain, and still am. To win the approval of

women was important to me. Not to use some of the talents with which I knew I was endowed was to lack fulfilment, and was in any case at times impossible.

This does not make for an easy life nor always for a happy one for oneself or for others. I envy those who can make a happy marriage which remains a romance throughout their lives, but I am not sure that I have met many of them. 'In order to be happy we must be virtuous, get rid of our prejudices, enjoy good health, have strong tastes and passions and keep our illusions' wrote Mme la Marquise du Châtelet, who lived with Voltaire for sixteen years. 'Most pleasure comes from illusions, and he who has lost them is seldom happy. Those moralists who think that we should rid ourselves of our passions and desires know nothing about happiness which chiefly comes from their satisfaction.'

19. Achievement, Depression, Disillusionment, Despair

1969

Geoffrey Jefferson and I were discussing the phenomenon of ageing one day, and I said that the realization of ageing is something which can come upon you quite suddenly. 'Yes,' he said, 'all the time life is in front of you, leading you on. It is the things you are going to do which matter. Then quite suddenly, you realize that the time has gone, and you say to yourself "so that was it, was it? This thing we call life. Is that all it was?"'

And so it is: the realization of ageing. But it can come at different times for different things. I had always meant to give up the Chair of Medicine before retiring age, for the pace of modern medicine is such that you cannot continually keep up with the young men, especially if by now you have taken on some national responsibilities requiring other talents. The presidency of the Royal College of Physicians gave me the opportunity of doing this, while remaining a part-time physician and teacher. I also gave up the Medical Research Council, but the college required qualities of a kind which I think I still had. Even this I gave up at a time when I could have stayed on, for I have seen too many men hold out beyond the years of their usefulness. But the qualities of judgment remain and you may still be wanted in jobs which require judgment, diplomacy, or chairmanship, guided by the knowledge and expertise of others.

I still had the ambition that when I gave up the more demanding professional appointments I should devote more time to music, go back to the first principles of 'cello playing and try to become a more professional performer. This to some extent I have done, partly under the tuition of my friend Sylvia who is really a viola-player but is expert in the basic principles of string playing. She has taken me back to the beginning to show me how to use a bow, which in my innocence and naïveté I thought I had learnt in 1909. Perhaps Sylvia in addition to understanding the principles of string playing also understands me.

My tone, and my command of the instrument have improved immensely, but as they do so, the finger-joints of my left hand become more tender and I find myself avoiding the little finger because at best it lacks strength, and at worst it is painful. So my F sharp on the C string tends to be not quite sharp enough unless I make a conscious effort regardless of discomfort, and sometimes I finger the fourth position 1 2 3 instead of 1 3 4, and when I wake in the night one of the many causes of my profound depression is the conviction that soon I shall not be able to play at all or if I can, no one will want to play with me.

The protective mechanisms, the unconscious ones, come more and more into evidence. If you work at home there are always papers and letters which require attention, and some of them require no great effort and are agreeable tasks like replying to requests for your opinion—and it is nice still to be asked—or correspondence with friends and family, or a reply to your opponent's last move in the game of postcard chess you are currently playing; and you want to practise the 'cello. This is one of the things you really want to do, so that you can still go on improving, even in your seventieth year, but something catches your eye, something to file, perhaps, or to look up in *Who's Who*, or the need to telephone the garage, anything, it seems, the more trivial the better, which will keep you from the real task of taking out the 'cello, tuning it, practising scales and technique.

And then there are the waking in the night and the depression and the thoughts of suicide. To some extent they are endogenous, something built into your personality. If you didn't find one cause for depression there would be another. Your children are all abroad, your grandchildren are growing up as strangers, the news is terrible—everything is violence and war. The most powerful country in the Western world is dominated by crooks and thugs. Innocent people cannot walk in the streets of American cities; students who used to be fired with ideals and ambitions take to drugs and are interested only in protests and disturbances. Can we blame them as long as Vietnam lasts?

Yet the depression is to some extent inbuilt and hereditary. My brother has something of it. My mother in her sixties, still in demand as a supervisor of school practice, told me how she would lie awake in the early hours feeling that she could not face the anxieties of another day, and the long journey into the East End of London. She had arthritis in her hips, and walked with a stick. This, she said, was very helpful, for everyone was willing to give you a seat and assist you on and off the buses, but it had one disadvantage—if you carried a stick everyone seemed to think that you must be deaf, and would talk to you in their loudest voice. But when the morning actually came and she had to face the day, it somehow did not seem so difficult after all.

The protective mechanisms of the mind put up a barrier of inertia against all kinds of creative work, even writing one's memoirs; there is always something else to do which requires little or no mental effort, emptying the waste-paper baskets, or filling the humidifier. None of this is really new. Like Jerome K. Jerome, 'I like work; it fascinates me. I can sit and look at it for hours.' At the height of one's powers there were always times of fatigue when the barriers against creative effort were too high to be overcome, but ten minutes, or perhaps half an hour of sleep would put that right. Even the suicidal thoughts of the night are not new. In all my most troubled times, even as a young man, I had thought of suicide as the ultimate friend to whom, in a time of extremity, I could look for the final solution.

So-called retirement, which means working at home without adequate secretarial assistance, is not easy either. You can spend a day out at work without any feeling of guilt, but if you spend a day working alone in your study, your wife's mounting resentment, though natural, pardonable and even unexpressed, permeates the atmosphere like a freezing fog. Yet all you may have done is the necessary homework for the various part-time jobs which help to bring in an adequate income. You have not even started on the jobs you want to do, such as personal writing or music.

Music makes a noise, so you cannot practise and pretend that you have been replying to letters; and you cannot practise late at night. But thinking and writing are often best done from 11 p.m. until 2 a.m. when all is quiet and no one is wanting you to do something else. Then you sit drinking sherry until the early hours and wake again at five more depressed than ever.

If only you could give up alcohol, perhaps things would seem better, but my brother says he has tried this and it is no use, and in times of depression and inertia it can be the one thing which changes your mood and makes it possible to be creative once more and write or dictate to the tape machine late into the night.

The years take on a more finite character. Having been born in 1900 the approaching year, 1970, seems to have a peculiarly sinister significance. In your fifties you are as good as ever, though perhaps you cannot play cricket—but you never could. In your sixties, if you choose the jobs you can still do well, you know you are ageing, but not yet deteriorating. But at seventy surely at last you can no longer disguise the fact that you are an old man. You develop symptoms which as a doctor you know may be trivial, but might be the beginning of internal cancer or heart failure, and you almost welcome them, for surely these are better alternatives than a steady decline into senility or a stroke that leaves you paralysed and useless. And so in the night, suicide once more becomes the obvious, even the logical solution.

The protective mechanisms step in again. I always keep enough barbiturate for the purpose, and I take it with me when I go away, but, as a rule, the recovery from the early morning depression is sufficient to drive away the suicidal thoughts and if they stay with you all day the mind finds some reason for saying 'not today'. You have a job on hand that you must complete first, or your Will must be rewritten.

Living with a psychiatrist doesn't make it any easier. I have always been interested in the psychological side of medicine, and my wife, whom I greatly admire, and whose real and rare skill in the treatment of mentally disturbed children I respect and acclaim, has taught me a great deal since she became a psychiatrist. Some of the concepts of psycho-analysis have helped me in my understanding of other people, but they can also be dangerous and destructive. Even a life of modest achievement requires a belief in oneself, which, even if irrational, is quite essential. I have tried to learn the things which I can do best and recognize those in which I have failed. If I have taken on some large and seemingly important tasks, it has not, I think been through a lust for power, but through a belief in myself, however misplaced, that I could do them better than anyone else. Without that belief I would not have been able to tackle the job.

Psycho-analysis, whether self-applied or just absorbed from the environment, may be important to people who want to be someone else, but can rob you of your self-esteem, of your idealistic belief in your own motivation and of the illusions which so often supply the dynamic power. I have always seen myself as a person who defied illness and carried on bravely, heedless of danger to health, life or limb, looking upon it as a weakness ever to take a day in bed. But this apparently is only a manifestation of my neurotic constitution and I could have achieved the same ends had I been a more stable personality, with much less expenditure of physical and mental energy.

If I feel deeply about a matter, it is due to some deep-seated prejudice and not to the idealistic thoughts which I cherish, and if this realization drives me into a state of frenzy, this turns out to be typical of those whose emotional development was arrested at the two-year-old level. This in turn is due to the unsatisfactory marital relationship of my parents. Sometimes I wish they had never met, let alone married. All in all, whoever you are, you would have been better to be someone else. But this, I confess, does not appeal to me. For all my failures, which become ever clearer to me, I do not think I ever want, or wanted to be someone else.

If my self-esteem and my vanity is all illusion, and my dearest desires, loves and inspirations have all been fantasy, I would still rather have had the experience of loving madly, adoringly and irrationally than not having known what love of this kind can mean; and to be finally robbed of all my illusions and fantasies can only bring me back to the recurring theme of my early morning waking, namely suicide. Perhaps that too is fantasy and will never come about. It has still to be put to the test. It is real enough at the time. But I would still rather live with it than subject myself to psychotherapy, which I fear would only rob me of any remaining shreds of self-esteem, fantasy and illusion, which in my more manic moods I am still able to save from the wreckage of what was once my personality.

This was written in 1969 and intended to be the end of the book.

1970: 'Der schwer gefasste Entschluss'

At last I made up my mind. At seventy I made a decision which many, perhaps most, may think unforgivable; for it could mean bringing grief and loneliness to one with whom I had shared so much for so long and had a duty to care for, to shield, support and respect. Or was this too, just my vanity, that to lose such a one as me might be beyond bearing? And now I have the admiration which, weak, vain creature that I am, I seem to need. Is it fantasy and illusion? Do I care, if the magic works?

The depression left me at once. Being contrite, even sad, sorry, worried, over the happiness of someone else is a state of different quality from black depression and despair. I found I could give up alcohol and became practically teetotal. In consequence I lost over a stone in weight in a few weeks. I was young again. I could walk uphill, run, carry a 'cello around in its fibre case without exhaustion, work and write. Strangely I can drink black coffee late at night and sleep like a child.

Even in small subconscious things my outlook changed; where before I had thought death not far away, I found that buying new clothes once more made sense. With every day packed with activity, working hard, playing hard, I yet found peace—not the peace of the dying but peace based on a new hope and a new faith in myself. 'Neue Kraft fühlend' as Beethoven wrote on the gay hopeful interludes of that wonderful slow movement of the A minor quartet, a thanksgiving for his recovery. Alas it was not a recovery for long in his case, for his illness was a mortal one.

I cannot recommend others to do what I did. It is a decision which must rarely if ever be right, but it may have saved my life; and I hope that the one whom I left may still forgive me, perhaps has done so already. Like Harvey, 'I fear lest I have mankind at large for my enemies ... still the die is cast and my trust is in the love of truth and the candour of cultivated minds.'

On the last movement of his last string quartet Beethoven wrote 'Der schwer gefasste Entschluss. Muss es sein? Es muss sein.' I know of no satisfactory translation into English. 'The with-difficulty arrived-at resolution. Must it be? It must be', is a translation but it is hardly English. With more respect for the message than for the words we might say: 'The dread decision: Must it be? It must be.'

No one seems to know what Beethoven's dilemma was, but this quartet was written in the last year of his life. The music which asks the question 'Must it be?' is strident and terrifying. The music which tells of the decision made, or perhaps of the inevitable accepted, is lively, hopeful, and has lost its terror. But indecision recurs for a time, even more discordantly than before, and the themes become frighteningly mixed, the violins saying 'It must be', while viola and 'cello still ask 'Must it be?' Gradually the hopeful theme emerges but goes again through a grave but brief period of doubt before the final return to serenity.